The Resilience Template

---

7 Steps to Improve Your Mental Health

Carol Hickson
www.resiliencetemplate.com

The Resilience Template – 7 Steps to Improve Your Mental Health

By Carol Hickson

LetGoBeHappy Publishing

First Printing: March 2021

ISBN Print Book: 978-1-8384088-0-0

Carol Hickson – Therapist, Life Coach and Workplace Resilience Trainer

Cheshire, UK.

www.resiliencetemplate.com

www.carolhickson.co.uk

0044 7899806494

carol@carolhickson.co.uk

PC: Simon Raeburn Photography

Carol Hickson is a Clinical Hypnotherapist, Emotional Freedom Technique Practitioner, Life Coach, Mindfulness Teacher, and Reiki Practitioner. She is a volunteer Clinical Hypnotherapist for Anxiety UK. She has a Bachelor of Arts degree in Education and is a former teacher of modern foreign languages.

Carol became a therapist following her own struggle with insomnia and chronic back pain. She created *The Resilience Template – 7 Steps to Improve Your Mental Health* originally as a series of community classes. She is a contributing author to the book *Mindfulness for Transformation* by Shamash Alidina and the Teach Mindfulness Community. Carol is committed to sharing her knowledge to help others improve their mental health.

Carol has three adult children and lives in Cheshire, UK, with her partner Rich and their two Bordoodle dogs Cozumel and Beeston. When not working she loves reading, gardening, and listening to live music.

Carol Hickson is available for mental health and resilience workshops, CPD training or to speak at your business event. Call (0044)7899806494, email carol@carolhickson.co.uk or visit www.carolhickson.co.uk for booking information.

Why Read This Book

If you have ever struggled with anxiety and stress then this book is for you. Too many of us mistakenly believe that we are broken when in fact we are merely stuck. Stuck in old replays of past stories. Stuck in fear of what happens next. Stuck because we cannot see the way forward. This book shows you how to become unstuck and in doing so you become an engineer on the roller coaster of life.

The stigma around mental health has existed for far too long. Only now are we beginning to wake up to the realisation that the sticking plaster approach cannot continue. We need real solutions to real problems.

In this book, Carol shares the four pillars of resilience and the 7 PARTNER steps which help build and maintain those pillars. The book explains, challenges, and encourages you to make better decisions as you move forward with your life.

In this book, you will find simple explanations of the physiological mechanism that perpetuates your stress. Armed with this knowledge you will then learn how to neutralise the stress response and introduce a *mental hygiene routine* into your life which over time will become as natural to you as your dental hygiene routine.

This book does not offer an easy fix, but if you have lived

with stress and anxiety you are already stronger and more capable than you might think. People living with stress and anxiety are not weak despite what you may previously have been led to believe. This inherent strength will help you make the daily changes required to transform your life.

At the end of this book, you will have a toolbox of exercises and techniques which will help you in any situation which you might previously have deemed stressful. Use the toolbox to build a lifeboat and sail into your life expecting storms but confident in your ability to deal with them.

You can access free resources and guided meditations from this book at www.resiliencetemplate.com

What others are saying about this book

‘Carol has faced considerable hardships in her life and has had to find a way to cultivate resilience and heal her body and mind. In the last few years, she has found a variety of approaches that have worked for both her and her clients. She has skillfully compiled these highly practical techniques into a Resilience Template that all can now use. I love the way she weaves stories and metaphors into this book, so all the exercises and ideas are brought to life. I recommend this book to anyone going through challenges, looking to understand their difficulties and seeking practical solutions they can apply in their lives today.'

-Shamash Alidina

Mindfulness for Dummies

‘In The Resilience Template, Carol Hickson has provided us with a uniquely helpful book. The book is equal parts inspiration, information, and practical experimentation. The exercises allow the reader to move beyond merely reading the book and into engagement with the power of the ideas she presents. I wish I had written this book!'

- Graham Old
The Anxiety Guide:
Self-Help for the Rest of Us

Dedications

For Rebecca, Liam, and Cieran. I hope you feel a fraction of the pride on seeing this book published as I feel each day when I think of you.

For Richard too, who supports, encourages and constantly tells me that I can do this even on the days when I'm not entirely sure. Everybody needs a Richard in their life.

The Resilience Template™ was an idea that began in Northwich, Cheshire before the Covid-19 lockdown. A group of people answered the call to come together and develop skills to create a better mindset. The results were great, the participants were even greater and because of them this book was written. I am forever grateful to them.

Table of Contents

Chapter 1

❦

The Beginning

'It is not in the stars to hold our destiny but in ourselves.'

William Shakespeare

What do you do when you find yourself submerged by the past or constantly swimming against the current of the future? Do you capitulate and float aimlessly along? Do you concede control for the consequences and decisions in your life, or resign yourself to a poorer experience? Or do you grab on to tools and build yourself a lifeboat? Do you accept responsibility for escaping the shallows so that you can have the joy of sailing in the glorious waters of life? And back on dry land, do you share the lifeboat with others whom you meet? So that the shoreline fills with people who have transformed their lives too.

Within this book, you will find the tools to build your lifeboat so that you can navigate towards the life that you choose rather than towards a life that you feel you have inherited. If you are ready to learn how to thrive in your natural habitat, read on.

The Resilience Template™ is my practical contribution to the improvement of mental health. It is built on difficult personal experiences, time spent in therapy as a client, and my professional experience as a successful therapist and mental resilience trainer. In the last few years, the profile of mental health has been raised. However, there is still a stigma around poor mental health. We are often embarrassed to admit to having problems and fearful of how a diagnosis might impact our employment prospects. Compare this to the reaction to a physical condition, and it seems strange. Imagine if, instead of focusing on recovery, your main concern was hiding from other people's judgement; it would hardly be a basis for healing, neither is it for mental health.

The Resilience Template™ is a toolbox for those of us trying to manage stress and mental health. Even before the fear caused by Covid-19 and the restrictions placed upon us as individuals, the media had started to highlight issues. Young men particularly are deemed at risk. Whilst the resilience of our young men is undoubtedly a cause for concern, when it comes to mental health we cannot assume that there is only one face of the problem. There is a whole spectrum of people whose lives are restricted and unfulfilled. Parents are in therapy, children are in therapy, and we seem wary of addressing the fundamental problems. At an elementary level, many of us seem to have lost the skill of resilience, and as a result, we find it difficult to manage life.

For many the modern lifestyle comprises long working hours, poor diet, and irregular exercise. We live increasingly materialistically, and the result is that we often find ourselves juggling the debt we incur. Life has become a takeaway bubble, whether that be food, entertainment, or relationships and herein lies the problem because it is a lifestyle built on sand. It is unsustainable because it cannot sustain us long term. We need more.

For those who have been experiencing the stress response since childhood, there seems to be an even bigger issue. A few years ago, I completed the Adverse Childhood Experience (ACE) questionnaire; the term was created by researchers Vincent Felitti, Robert Anda, and their colleagues in 1995. The questionnaire asks ten questions about possible traumatic experiences up to the age of eighteen. Each positive response scores a point; the premise is that if you score at least 6 out of 10, and if you have not learnt positive interventions then you may experience high-risk health issues or even die earlier than your peers, due to cumulative stress. I fall into that category, but I had no idea until I was in my 50s and trying to find a way through insomnia and physical health problems. Only then did I truly begin to understand the extent to which our mental health impacts our physical health and vice versa.

Bruce Lipton, a respected cell biologist and the author of *Biology of Belief* (1988), cites research from Stanford University indicating that stress is the causal factor of 95 per cent of all illness and disease. Sit with that figure a moment. Ninety-five per cent of all disease and illness has a root in stress. We can use this information to make intelligent decisions about whether stress is an inconvenience or a likely killer because it seems we have a hitman on our tail, and we need to go to serious lengths to protect ourselves.

I wonder how things might have been different if I had known, when younger, that many of the physical problems that I had were linked to my emotional health, and this was a product of childhood trauma and stress. When I was off work with menorrhagia, back problems, and insomnia, perhaps I could have healed sooner had the link between my emotional and physical pain been identified.

Along with many other people, I was born to parents who could not cope. I cannot judge them, I loved my parents but they had their own demons, and they never came to terms with their own childhood traumas. We know that without positive intervention, generations have a habit of repeating the same mistakes. Knowing that is one thing, but not doing more now to help people move beyond these ancestral handcuffs is not good enough. We are beyond box-ticking exercises and banal commentaries on the state of our mental health.

You would think that, in a world where fifty years ago we put a man on the moon and transplanted a heart from one human to another, we might be ready to tackle mental health by using more than just platitudes. Take the strapline used across one of the big TV channels recently, *Get Britain Talking*. The advice: stop what you're doing and chat with the person next to you. I found myself getting increasingly exasperated; what a missed opportunity. To have the mainstream media engaged, with access to millions of people, and then not to share practical tools is frustrating. Especially as we have tools which we know can make a difference to improve mental health. Do not get me wrong, it is good to talk, but it is not even going to leave a scratch on the surface of what's happening in the minds of many people. If all it takes is to find somebody during the adverts and talk, so many of us might have avoided the personal investment, over the years, of time, health, and money spent in therapy. And if it is simply a matter of talking to the person next to me, then surely by talking to professionals, I should have got over my *stuff* years ago because they're trained to deal with people like me, aren't they?

This missed opportunity for concrete action has made me more determined to share my knowledge beyond my private sessions and group work. If you sense some anger here, there is. Lives are blighted by poor mental health, and lives are lost to it. We are *so* past the sticking plaster phase in this country, telling us to go off and chat is akin to saying, 'You've got gangrene in that limb? Silly you! You need to wash it under a tap.' Or in the case of my four-year bout of insomnia, 'You haven't slept properly in four years, oh you just need to put a few lavender drops on your pillow.'

This book is part of the curriculum we were not taught in school. It explains how many of us living with stress and anxiety are running the fight or flight survival mode. I was 50 before I began to recognise this response in myself and then in my clients. I did not discover this, experts have written about it, but I have found that breaking the stress/survival response down to its fundamental components has changed my clients' lives. A stressed mind, an anxious mind, a mind swept up in fight or flight, lacks coherence. Stress clouds our judgement. Stressed thinking diverts and distracts us, and the result is that we do not always make the best decisions or live the best life.

I am not a doctor, and I always advise clients first to seek medical advice, but I have spent several years researching stress and resilience as a therapist. This book aims to simplify what we already know. It provides information, explanation, techniques, exercises, and suggestions for a daily framework on which to hang tools to improve mental fitness and change mindset. It provides a toolbox of techniques that are easy to practise at home. This is important because if you have ever been to an exercise class, you will know that initially, it can be difficult to learn the routines. In class, you participate, but once you get home, often your mind goes blank, and you struggle to remember what to do. This also happens for therapy clients. Everything seems clear during a session but committing the exercises to memory and adopting a daily routine can be confusing. People do not give up trying to change their mindset because of a lack of motivation; they give up because they feel overwhelmed and do not yet understand how the mind works.

When I realised this, I created The Resilience Template™. I believe the tools in this book have changed the trajectory of my life, and that they can do the same for you. The Resilience Template™ will provide you with a structure and a plan, and your contribution to making it work will be daily repetition, and consistency. Keep reading because once you understand how the brain embeds patterns, you will see how steady, daily practice will change your life. As new neural connections in the brain fire and wire together, eureka, everything will change!

Chapter 2

❧

How to Use This Book

'Be the change you wish to see in the world.'

Mahatma Gandhi

This self-help book contains many of the tools that I use during one-to-one and group resilience sessions. As in so many other areas of our life, mental health is not a spectator sport – it requires active participation.

You will need to keep a journal because I will ask you to write down your own experiences as we progress. By the time we get to the daily techniques later in the book, you will already have committed many reflections and aspirations to paper.

The book will work best if you follow the chapters sequentially.

Build the techniques up slowly. It is better to do a few well than the bulk of them badly. The exercises to calm the nervous system in the preparation chapter, Chapter 7, are essential; spend a minimum of 21 days practising these before moving on. Initially, you could practise them by breaking your day into four sections, morning, lunchtime, after work, and before bed, and allocate 15 minutes of practice time to each block. You are building mental fitness, and like any fitness routine, it is best not to overcomplicate it. Little and often is the mantra.

In the following chapters I will share tools to help you build a lifeboat which will move you from stuck to transformation.

Chapter 3 covers mental resilience and how we can develop this in our lives. It offers an opportunity for reflection for those of us raising children, and if you choose, you can share the tools with them to help them navigate life better. This chapter also sets out the four pillars which I believe underpin resilience: Flexibility, Pragmatism, Planning, and Action. Developing these four areas will improve your resilience.

Chapter 4 links stress and anxiety to the primitive survival response and compares the physiological fight or flight response with stress and anxiety symptoms. Viewed side by side, we can see the commonality of reactions. It includes a description of anxiety symptoms; these move us away from the stereotypical description of an anxious person, which, at best, can be misleading and, at worst, damaging to our long-term health. There are some questions to consider as we take a holistic view of modern life. Work through this chapter slowly and record your responses in your journal.

Chapter 5 considers motivations for change, and this chapter will show why planning is important. Think of your mind as having an internal satnav; this leads you to the destination on which you are most focused. Participate by taking time to consider the questions asked; each of us has individual motivations and aspirations. Using your journal will help you make this a personal process to transform your life.

Chapter 6 introduces my rationale for creating the programme. I also share the PARTNER steps to mental fitness, which are based on my professional experience. I have used The Resilience Template™ with individuals and in group sessions, and the results are encouraging.

Chapter 7 addresses the necessity for good preparation when undertaking a task. As a minimum, spend 21 days practising the techniques in this chapter. During this time, familiarise yourself with the exercises and use them at least four times a day. Expect to feel uncomfortable doing some of the exercises; all change involves a departure from our comfort zone. If you are pregnant or have a breathing condition, then please consult a doctor before undertaking the exercises.

The questions around your felt safety, simply how safe and grounded you feel, are important, and I would recommend that you return to them frequently, noting down any successes and working on any areas where you continue to feel stuck. Only when you have begun to feel safe, which you might recognise as feeling calmer, and less reactionary should you move to the next chapter. By then, you will have prepared the ground to accept the seedlings of change. As we move through subsequent chapters and introduce new techniques, continue too with the exercises in Chapter 7. By addressing limiting beliefs about yourself, and the world, you are potentially undoing years of outdated programming, relinquishing poor habits and self-sabotaging thoughts, and installing better ones. To do this well it is important that you develop and then maintain a strong sense of grounding and safety. Just like acquiring a 'gym' body, once you have achieved better mental fitness, the work continues to maintain it.

In Chapter 8, we focus on acceptance. Acceptance of the past, of difficult experiences and feelings, is not to be confused with resignation. When we decide to accept, we are not adding to any feelings that make us a victim; instead, acceptance is the hammer that breaks the shell of those feelings. Once we accept, we take back the power from other people; no longer can they hurt us because we no longer subjugate ourselves to their judgement, opinions, or behaviour. Acceptance is the propane that fuels us towards a better future. Again, spend time on this section. Consider and reflect on the questions. Lack of acceptance is often the quicksand that keeps us stuck. If this process is too difficult for you to do alone, please consider enlisting the help of a therapist.

Chapter 9 focuses on reconnection. When was the last time you stopped and truly listened to your body? To the quality and content of your thoughts? Or to consider what is most important to you? Many of us manage to ignore our problems by distraction and denial. In this chapter, as you learn how to tune back in, you can update any old programming that is not working. Think of your computer, if it had not had an update for years how would it be running? Likewise the mind.

Chapter 10 looks at the quality of our self-talk. So many of our internal voices are disrespectful and rude. If we spoke to other people in the way that we talk to ourselves, we would likely find ourselves unemployable and friendless. With the information in this chapter, our internal communication becomes kinder and more compassionate.

Chapter 11 reminds us that the only time we can live a fulfilled life is now. Too many of us live regretting the past or projecting *what-ifs* ahead of us, forgetting that no one is promised a future. Focusing on the present, on actually *what-is* rather than *what-if* and being mindful of our quality of living is a fundamental element in changing our lives. We live in the moment because nothing else is a given.

In Chapter 12, I help you to create a personalised schedule, based on your existing habits, on which to hang the techniques. This chapter is the *how* that I promised you in Chapter 5. It will make it easier for you to install change consistently and diligently throughout your day.

Chapter 13 is an opportunity to reflect. Change is not linear; we are not one dimensional, our values change, our aspirations too, and reflection encourages us to check back in. Many of us think that we know what our problem is, but after reflection we often discover it is something entirely different. I encourage you to use a journal for daily reflection, summarising the positives at the end of each day, at the end of each week, and then at the end of each month. Change is often subtle, and we are more likely to recognise it when we maintain regular records.

Chapter 14 summarises what we have learnt and offers us a vision of our lives when we embrace change. We become calmer, more focused, and mentally resilient. Others may even notice before you do. The change in you will inspire other people to take responsibility and action for their own lives. The toolbox is shared, the lifeboat is built, transformation continues.

Chapter 3

✑

Resilience

'Every moment of light and dark is a miracle.'

Walt Whitman

Resilience. You see the word everywhere popping up in marketing slogans and education mission statements. The word is well used and yet less widely understood. I worry that overuse and lack of understanding will reduce it to a mere buzzword. During the Covid-19 pandemic experts have taken to the media to explain that we all need to be more resilient. But what if we do not know how to interpret the word? What does it mean? And what if we are looking outwards for fool's gold when the magic happens internally?

I cannot help but wonder if some of the lack of resilience that we see is linked to the lack of opportunities that children have had to step out of their parents' protective shield and experience some of the realities of life. I know that parents do a difficult job, but sometimes I worry that we overprotect our children rather than trusting ourselves, as their first teachers, and our children themselves. When I was young, we had so much more freedom than children have now. We had part-time jobs from age thirteen. We had responsibilities inside and outside the home. We spent our free time outside playing with friends and building relationships with other children in the locality. We had rules to follow and consequences if we didn't because our parents were authority figures rather than our friends.

I see parents who are worn out holding down full-time jobs, running households, and ferrying children to their hobbies. Often when I ask what help they get from their children at home they reply that they get none because it is easier to do it all themselves. In the long term, this option for an *easy* life does not work for parents or for children. It leaves the former exhausted and the latter often unable to manage simple tasks. It becomes the *hotel syndrome* where children make little or no contribution to the home and family life because their parents have decided either that it is not fair to ask them or it is more trouble than it is worth when you do ask them. Over time, this denies children opportunities to see what they are capable of, to contribute to family life, and to learn personal and familial responsibility.

Not only have we lost opportunities to demonstrate resilience in the home, but we have done the same in schools too. Some school sports days no longer celebrate winning, instead the emphasis focuses mainly on participation. Inclusion of all children is undoubtedly important but I am not sure that there should be reticence about celebrating success which comes in many forms. It seems counter-intuitive.

At parents' evening, when my children were younger, I remember a teacher saying that she was not allowed to say anything about my child that might be taken critically. I was flabbergasted; I just wanted an honest appraisal of my child's progress.

Some people complain, in derogatory terms, of the *snowflakes* – young people with an inflated sense of uniqueness, easily offended and unable to cope with any opposition, but I wonder if this is fair comment because I worry that we may have underprepared them. I feel for them because I honestly believe that excessive shielding, in the long-term, is a disservice to them and their capabilities.

As a child growing up in a dysfunctional household, I learnt to rely on myself. I had no idea at the time, but I carved myself a coping mechanism, which I recognise now as resilience. I got involved locally in the community, aged thirteen I took a part-time job, and I worked hard at school. This external focus showed me a world beyond what was happening within the family home, and it gave me a vision of a better future. Without fully understanding, and despite the turbulence of home life, I could always get back up on my feet, and I have been grateful ever since for this skill.

When my children were younger there was a pop song that resonated with me for two reasons. Firstly, the absolute joy with which the children responded, dropping to the floor and up again, as they danced until they were light-headed. Secondly, I realised that it was an anthem for resilience, a shout out for people going through life's storms. The song is *Tubthumping* by Chumbawamba:

'I get knocked down, but I get up again. You are never gonna keep me down.'

This is resilience; it is an anthem for motivation and hope. No matter what you are living through, resilience is what gets you back on your feet. When the rug has been pulled from beneath you, resilience propels you forward because when you are resilient, you intrinsically understand that life is for living.

The good news is that because resilience is a skill, we can all improve it, and this starts with understanding exactly what is being asked of us. I believe that resilience has four main pillars: Flexibility, Pragmatism, Planning, and Action.

Flexibility

At the core of resilience is flexibility. Like a tree in the wind, we get buffeted, and although we bend, we do not break. We frequently see resilience in nature, plants appear through the rubble on building sites, forests regenerate after terrible fires, and animals graze in the harshest conditions. Having resilience does not make us non-stick like a brand of coated cookware; unpleasant things still happen, and they can still hurt us. They can also teach us to appreciate our adaptability and our capacity for challenge, and this is priceless. Knowing that we have survived difficulties, which felt near impossible to bear at the time, provides us with evidence-based confirmation of our strength. No matter how vulnerable we feel, experience points to the truth that we will likely come through hard times because we have done so before. Think of your mind as a computer. This evidence becomes a vital addition to your survival database, the archive of your internal and external threat perception. Reminding yourself that you have coped with difficulties and challenges in the past is an essential plug-in to update your systems.

Despite our fears, we do usually come through bad times. We do not always come out unchanged, which is often no bad thing, but we often emerge wiser. Developing the ability and the strength to analyse and learn from what has happened, to take feedback from difficult times is part of being flexible. Too often, we rush to brush things away, to escape difficult memories, and to resume our lives. If we slip into old patterns simply to avoid thinking about problems, we lose feedback, which means we lose a possible growth opportunity.

Pragmatism

Pragmatism, too, is an essential component of resilience. Many of us have grown up watching Hollywood movies, and Disney films, believing in stories of 'happy ever after'. They often leave us unprepared for the challenges of living. More recently, many reality television programmes broadcast daily disillusionment and controlled misery directly into our homes. Pragmatism requires balance because life is not black and white; it is much more challenging and nuanced.

I see people who doubt themselves because life has not transpired as they expected it would. This is where balance is important because life is generally good, but that does not mean it is Disney-good. It has difficulties and trials. Sometimes though, they can turn out to be the best thing that ever happened. A few years ago, I was involved in a minor car accident. At the time, it was upsetting, but it changed my life for the better. It came during a week of personal upheaval. As a result of investigations to discover the reason for my four-year bout of insomnia, I was diagnosed with Dystonia and told that I had begun to paralyse down my left side. Three days after this, my family was involved in the car accident I mentioned. I suffered whiplash, compounding my existing spinal problems for which I held a disabled blue-badge. As I was self-employed, I had to stop working, and my income ceased. Three days afterwards, on Christmas Day, my mother died unexpectedly, and the next day my uncle died. The landscape of my life changed within less than a week.

With time on my hands, I realised that I had taken too much for granted, especially my health, because it is not a given, and I had neglected it for too long. I gave myself time to heal, physically, emotionally, and mentally and once I had committed, I was astonished at the speed of change in my life. The events that week were catalysts that transformed my life. I began to sleep again, my back and neck issues improved, and I eventually retrained as a therapist.

During difficult times especially, we might feel inclined to compare our lives with those of other people, but this is not realistic. When you compare yourself with somebody else, you build a theory based on a set of imagined assumptions. We cannot know the experiences that have shaped the people we meet and so we cannot make comparisons. When we resort to comparisons, the danger is that we can amplify our own problems because we have an emotional connection to our own pain and presume that others have had an *easier* life. A gentleman once asked me why his life was so hard. I asked if he thought that other people struggled, and he replied, 'No, not like me' but we cannot know how others have been affected by their experiences. We can only compare like for like, and each of us is unique. Resilient people are pragmatic enough to resist making comparisons.

Pragmatism teaches us that we all have trials and tribulations because life is a rollercoaster rather than a merry-go-round. Think of a resilient person as the engineer who repairs and recalibrates the roller coaster, the person who is both resourceful and ready. They seek out the light, and when darkness comes, they ride the storm knowing that sunshine lies beyond.

Without pragmatic realism, we are unprepared, and when things do not work out as we expected they would, many of us self-medicate using drugs, alcohol, and damaging relationships. Sadly, not only do we block out pain, but we also barricade ourselves against hope, and without hope we find ourselves stuck in an ever-increasing brand of dull and pointless living.

Planning

The third pillar of resilience is planning; we will look more at this in Chapter 5. We cannot live in isolation. We see pain, disease, and death on the news constantly.

I remember a primary school lesson when our teacher asked, 'What is the one certainty in life?' and the answer was that 'We are going to die.' It is inevitable. Our bodies will deteriorate, and we may experience pain and illness. We will lose people who we love or watch them suffer as we stand by helpless. We will win and lose jobs; we will have hopes dashed. This is the tapestry of life.

When we hear of tragedies happening to others, if we have not had similar experiences, we can have little comprehension of their pain. When challenging events happen to us, many of us are unprepared. It is as though we have been bowled a curveball.

I have a personal theory about human beings: until we experience things for ourselves, many of life's problems pass over our heads. Take grief, for example. Some of us do not experience loss early in life. On the one hand, that is our great good fortune, but on the other, it means that we have little comprehension of loss and bereavement. When my partner died of a brain tumour, aged fifty-four, I remember being shocked by the realisation that people did not seem to understand; they just did not seem to 'get it', and to me in my grief, they appeared cold. Several years later, a relative lost her partner, and her pain was palpable; it was like her pain had opened a window on a world that she had never imagined. If we faced these inevitabilities of life in our culture, without becoming maudlin, we could develop the resilience to be comfortable with others in their pain. Perhaps, it might seem too hard to bear, but I think that it would improve our own experience. If we allow ourselves to contemplate the certain challenges ahead, we might take more joy in the good times as they happen. Perhaps the saying 'If you have never experienced the dark, how can you appreciate the light?' might genuinely resonate.

So, resilience means that we plan for good and bad times, which means trusting ourselves to cope with misfortune and knowing that not only do we create a plan B but a plan C, D, and E if required.

Action

Action is the fourth component of resilience. When we are resilient, we cannot be passive. Resilient people are people of action. By that, I do not mean that they are jumping out of airplanes and bungee jumping, although they can. I mean that they do not expect the world to change for them. They do not sit passively waiting for things to be different because they do not expect that life will work for or against them; they accept that life just happens. They understand that the onus is on them to live the best life that they can. Neither are they reactive; reactive people rail against the world, focusing on problems and missing the opportunities for resolution. It is not the uncertainties in life that cause problems, they have always been there, it is our reaction to them and our subsequent behaviour. We cannot stop the events of life unfolding but we can change how we respond and not make a drama out of a crisis.

Picture two people in a restaurant served by the same waiter, eating the same meals. One is there with family and friends to celebrate getting an all-clear from a health scare. The food is reasonable, and the group leaves a small tip. The other person has just argued with his wife, and in his anger, he lashes out at the waiter. He refuses to pay and summons the manager. His complaints fill the restaurant, and the manager agrees to write off the full bill. Still unhappy, the customer badmouths the restaurant for days, especially across social media. He justifies his behaviour by calling it 'name and shame' when it really is an excessive over-reaction. Following his departure, the waiter slips off into the back for a moment to compose himself and to check in with his wife, who is at home alone, having just lost their baby. And the manager sits down with a glass of something strong, wondering how he will pay this week's wages.

We often see unhappy people acting badly and taking their misery out on other people. True control is not choosing the events that happen to us; it is managing our responses and our reactions to them. It is recognising that when we lash out, we create a domino effect that ripples outward, affecting others.

Whilst the four pillars help us move forward, they also provide some context for the pain we have experienced in the past. As resilient people, we no longer get distracted by our old stories. They become feedback rather than destiny. Michael Bernard Beckwith is an author and motivational speaker, and his view of pain and suffering draws a clear distinction between the two. He observes that,

'Pain is inevitable, suffering is the story we tell ourselves about the pain.'

I used to think my story was important. I thought that it was a way that people would understand me, perhaps connect with me, and feel compelled not to judge me. People with anxiety symptoms often have a fear of being judged. My story became my cloak, a shield that I hid behind for a long time.

After my partner died, I told people what had happened, not to seek sympathy but to avoid judgement and perhaps elicit kindness. I was tired and exhausted, and some days I felt barely coherent. If I were at the supermarket, struggling to find the right money, or queuing in a shop, I'd say, 'I'm sorry, I've recently lost my partner.' After several months, my then thirteen-year-old son gently asked me why I told strangers what had happened.

While a part of me felt judged and wanted to protest that he wasn't being fair, I knew that he was entirely right. I was using it to shield myself from criticism or judgement. After all, knowing that I was recently bereaved would stop any decent person from thinking badly of me, wouldn't it?

Since then, I have met lots of people who do the same. There is comfort and familiarity in the story. We know the narrative by heart, and it gives us the possibility to avoid more criticism. Often, where there is a story, there is a person desperate not to be judged.

Our story can become almost a rite of passage, and whilst it can be the best teacher we ever have, it can also become a millstone weighing us down and holding us back.

Our stories are chapters in the book of our life. They do not define or restrict us unless we choose to constantly play them on repeat and allow that to happen.

Imagine if you read a biography of your early life, and afterwards, it formed the backdrop to everything you ever said, thought, or believed about yourself for the next thirty years or more. The relevance of the tale would quickly wear out. It would become a very thin story, tired and familiar to all of those around you.

Perhaps, you would think that nobody has had a worse time and that everybody would understand you better if they knew what you had been through. Of course, some of us have had long periods of absolute pain in our lives, but suffering comes from the regular re-runs we give the memories of pain.

Resilient people understand that we choose the box set

videos we play in our minds. If you were at the cinema watching a terrible film, you could walk out. Likewise, at home, if there is a particularly bad programme on the television, you can switch it off. Now, there is a conundrum here; we might counteract the thought of *I don't have to watch this* with another that argues, *But I've paid for it, so I might as well watch it.* I think many of us do the same with the re-runs we play in our minds. If we stop screening this painful story from our past, then what a waste. It happened to us, and so it should be screened in full technicolour, no matter if it upsets us or keeps us stuck; it is the truth, and we can't pack the truth away in a cupboard for our convenience. But a lot of people do. They pick and choose which of their souvenirs have pride of place on the mantlepiece, the reminders of their life displayed around their homes. We display keepsakes of happy times, reminders of good memories, and trinkets that make us smile, bringing back some moments of happiness. Yet, in our minds, we recreate the darkest, miserable events of our lives, and we replay them regularly. This crutch anchors us to the past no matter that we haven't been that person, in that situation, for twenty, thirty, forty years, or more.

The game *Telephone* is a good example of how the mind works. The game starts with one statement, and by the time the final person repeats the sentence, the message is often different from the original message. Our minds too often distort our memories over time. The facts, which are so clear, may not have happened in quite the way that we now think we remember them. That is not to say that I dispute anyone's life story, but our minds constantly trawl their databases to find elements that support the story in whichever form fits. This is not deliberate subterfuge played out in devious minds, but simply the way our mind acquires information to fit its own beliefs.

Some of us mistakenly believe that holding onto the story gives us some control, but it does not. It is the story that controls us. If you feel you should always be in control, then you will inevitably be disappointed. There are so many uncertainties; environmental, health, familial, romantic, political, the list is endless. We cannot even control the parade of random thoughts and spontaneous sensations that regularly unsettle us and trying to is like fighting the tide. It is completely beyond our control. Instead of being afraid of uncertainties, imagine if we could learn to view them as possibilities for growth and change? We might then learn to appreciate challenges rather than seek to avoid them.

Life inevitably has highs and lows. How we respond to them and how we prepare our children for them is what matters. If this sounds melancholy, then I have failed to express myself. The thrill of being alive is not the promise of an *easy* life; it is having the resilience to accept where it takes you. Resilience is having the ability to stock up the store cupboard of good times, which can then be drawn from during difficult times. A client once asked me, 'Aren't you afraid of dying?' I replied, 'I'm afraid of not living.' If we get living right, then death will be just a tiny element of the vast tapestry we have woven and which we will leave as our legacy.

Chapter 4

∾

Stress and Anxiety

'Now is the age of anxiety.'

WH Auden

I sincerely believe that this is the most useful chapter in this book because it provides the key to unlocking how we manage stress. Before considering the benefits of The Resilience Template™ and how we can develop a resilient mindset, it is important to understand stress and anxiety because stress is a fundamental detractor from a peaceful mind. Stress is the automatic survival response initiated by our brain to a perceived threat. It is the call to arms signalling our bodies to prepare for danger. On the other hand, persistent anxiety is a mental health condition that can be triggered by stress, but it can also exist in the absence of stress. Despite what some people may think, neither of them point to weakness. At points in our lives, we may all experience stress and anxiety.

Perhaps the most fundamental piece of my recovery came in understanding that there was an underlying physiological process in action. The fight or flight response was running regularly. This was not something that I was deliberately bringing on myself. I was not weak, broken, or work-shy; I was reacting to an automatic response in my brain. This knowledge liberated me from the guilt and shame caused by my anxiety.

Many of us are familiar with the fight or flight survival response from science lessons at school, but even so, few of us realise that our bodies are engaged in the response during stressful periods. Put into this context, we can see that stress symptoms are an automatic response from the brain as it prepares the body to fight or run for survival. Understanding this changes our perception of both stress and anxiety at a fundamental level, seeing them as physiological responses to potential danger and not weakness.

The fight or flight response is a biological response to something perceived by the brain as a threat. The response itself comes from the part of our brain called the limbic system, which has changed little since we were cavemen. It is the part of the brain which perceives a threat and prepares our bodies to either run or fight for survival. It does this by flooding our system with hormones that activate the body's sympathetic nervous system. These stimulate the adrenal glands to produce adrenaline and noradrenaline, which cause internal changes increasing blood pressure, heart rate, and blood sugar levels. Now engaged, the digestive system slows as energy is diverted to areas where the first response is vital. Our legs are now prepared to run, our arms ready to defend ourselves, and all of this happens below our level of conscious thinking.

This response sits at the root of many stress reactions. It is true that most of us will never find ourselves in life-or-death situations but remember that we mentioned a *perceived* threat. Our primitive brain is working on old data. Instead of sabre tooth tigers, think about work pressure, health concerns, relationship issues, financial worries, and so on. Stress is cumulative, and whilst many of us will not have experienced the bigger life events, also known as *large T* traumas, the smaller ones can build up over time. The result is that, without a relief valve, pressure builds, and we find ourselves stuck longer in the primitive survival response.

This is an important point to make because many people believe that their response to stress means that part of them is broken or not working properly. This is not the case. Think of a smoke alarm warning us of the possibility of fire. We want to be able to rely on the alarm to respond quickly in case of an emergency. But if the smoke alarm sounds every time someone makes toast, you might decide that the alarm is unreliable. Perhaps, you would choose to replace it with a less sensitive model. Likewise, with our internal alarm system. When we actively change our behaviour and our reactions to problems, we calm the stress and begin to desensitise the system. We still need the survival response, it keeps us from mindlessly stepping into danger, but we implement calming techniques to ensure it is only running when appropriate. Would you ever consider leaving your car running overnight just in case you need to make a quick start in the morning? No, that would be unnecessary, and it would quickly cause engine damage. In the same way, we teach the survival response how to stand down.

We do this because our own survival response can become a danger to us if it is engaged long-term. The fight or flight reaction is not designed to run indefinitely. As a primitive response if we met a predator, we were killed, or we escaped, and the incident was resolved one way or the other. The threat to us nowadays is that smaller stressors are ongoing, there is not usually an end point which stops the production of adrenaline and cortisol and long term these increase the risk of inflammation and more serious health problems. If the symptoms we associate with stress and anxiety are the iceberg as it appears above water, for example, a beating heart, fidgeting, nausea, and so on, then the consequences of it running long-term lie beneath the surface. Survival response hormones course through our bodies, and long term, these cause damage. As mentioned in the first chapter, 95 per cent of disease has a root link to stress. This includes cancers and heart problems.

Think about what would happen to your central heating system if the thermostat malfunctioned and the system stayed on permanently. Your home would get hotter, and as the system was not designed to run without regulation for a sustained period, it would likely break down. To deal with the problem effectively, you interrupt the malfunction as soon as you realise there is a rise in temperature. If, however, you ignore or fail to recognise the problem, then there is a likelihood that some components will burn out, causing a bigger problem. This sensation of being burnt out is familiar to people who are impacted by stress and anxiety. Instead of central heating, think about the central nervous system, and you begin to understand why it is essential that we learn how to maintain and recalibrate the system.

Even more distressing is that, as humans, our children model our behaviour. By not resolving stress in our lives, not only are we potentially damaging our long-term health, but we are also teaching our children to do the same. This is another reason why we must learn to recognise and then deactivate the fight or flight response.

When we compare the fight or flight response to symptoms associated with stress, the picture becomes clearer. Consider the table of symptoms below:

Fight or Flight Response	Anxiety & Stress Symptoms
Heart beats faster	Heart palpitations
Blood pressure increases	Dizziness
Eyes – the pupils dilate	Staring eyes
Lungs breathe more quickly	Breathlessness
Saliva flow decreases	Dry mouth
Muscles tense	Trembling and restlessness
Digestive enzymes decrease	Stomach issues
Bowel–food movement slows	Bowel issues including IBS

In the fight or flight column, I have listed some of the effects of the substances produced by the survival response on the body and then compared these effects with symptoms commonly reported in stress and anxiety. The direct correlation between the two is clear.

Once I realised that I was running the fight or flight response, my health issues began to make sense. I then understood that firstly, and most importantly, I needed to find ways to disengage the survival reaction. When the fight or flight response is running, there is a reduction of up to 80 per cent in blood flow to the pre-frontal cortex, which is the thinking brain, this accounts for the brain fog many of us feel during stressful periods. Any attempts to create change prematurely, before taking steps to disengage the stress response, simply add to the chaos and will likely fail. So, the first step is to calm fight and flight and then implement change.

Many of us have seen the fight or flight response in action recently. It may have even affected us personally. Oddly, it featured toilet rolls. Do you remember the hunter-gatherers who stripped the shelves bare at the start of the Covid-19 pandemic? We saw images on television of scarcity and panic as food and toilet rolls disappeared at an alarming rate. Despite rational appeals for calm, people stocked up their shopping trolleys as if they would never shop again. They were caught in the fight or flight response. There was little rationality, little cognitive processing because they were seized by the survival impulse. The result was that, for weeks, some people had no idea where their next toilet rolls were coming from, whilst others knew exactly where they were; piled up on shelves in their garages. Does what you witnessed, or even did, make more sense when you think fight or flight response? Nobody is immune.

Stress can be both positive and negative. Eustress, or positive stress, often motivates us to do better. Physical stress at the gym can be positive because it releases endorphins, making us feel good; it can lower stress hormones like cortisol. However, as we will see later in this chapter, there are times when it might be best to avoid gym stress and instead elicit some calm and recalibrate our systems.

Eustress has a better-known negative counterpart known as distress, often accompanied by feelings of overwhelm and inability to cope. Distress can fall into two main categories: acute and chronic. These describe the difference between small transient stressors that crop up regularly in our lives, like traffic annoyances, and the bigger stressors like death and divorce, which are often more prolonged and affect us over a longer period. Recognising that, just like picking up the common cold, there will be times when we will have increased stress and anxiety can help us to manage the symptoms we experience.

Imagine if, from the time we were conceived, we had a bucket. Into this bucket went every stressful event we or our mother carrying us, ever experienced. This will vary from individual to individual. As we grew up, if we were taught how to manage these experiences or learnt outlets for our stress, our buckets would not overfill. If not, stress would pile on top of stress, and at some point, our buckets might become so full that they spill over. This is when stress impacts our lives and affects our ability to cope. The saying 'the straw that broke the camel's back' sums it up completely. It is not always the latest issue that is the problem but the cumulative effect of stress over time. Sometimes people try to deeply analyse what went wrong. They find themselves caught up trying to work out why something small has caused them to react badly and this overthinking adds to the overwhelm. Sometimes, we simply accept that there might not be a single causal factor because stress is cumulative.

Some people use exercise to manage stress, and, at times, that can be the right response. At other times though, exercising an already stressed mind and body can create additional strain because exercise produces adrenaline and cortisol, just as work stress or personal stress does. To a body that is already experiencing symptoms like a raised heartbeat, restlessness, and chaotic thinking, excessive exercise can compound the problem. At times like these, I ask clients whether it might be beneficial to cut down their gym attendance in the short term. It is a question of balance because we also know that stress can be a motivator, and that is why it is important to learn how to recognise your own signs of stress. This means looking at life from a holistic perspective and considering your diet, exercise routine, relaxation opportunities, and mindset.

Despite greater mental health media coverage, I find that people do not always recognise the signs of stress and anxiety in themselves. There is almost a stereotype that has developed into a caricature. Stress and anxiety do not always look like the Mavis Riley character on *Coronation Street*; for those of you not old enough to remember, she was a simpering woman with a squeaky voice, worrying whether the sherbet lemons have become too soft. Stress and anxiety can look like that, but not always.

Stress and anxiety may drive the person who dislikes sitting down to a meal or watching television with the rest of the family. I remember my mother often ate her food standing up in the kitchen, apart from the rest of the family.

They might be present in the person who is unable to be still and enjoy their garden because there are always weeds to be pulled or plants to be deadheaded.

Stress and anxiety might show in the person who is constantly driven to clean the house or wash their car.

They may be present in the person talking or watching television whilst scrolling through social media. The person who finds it hard to focus on one thing.

They might be seen in the person who constantly works late into the night, answering emails at the weekends, and even taking work on holiday.

They might drive the perfectionist to always do better because nothing they produce is ever good enough for them.

They might be present in the people pleaser, who allows everybody to speak their mind and meekly accepts any poor behaviour that is doled their way.

You may see them in the person who never settles; flitting from relationship to relationship, or from job to job, or from place to place.

They might be visible in the person who cannot let a topic go but who gnaws at problems, like a dog with a bone.

Stress and anxiety can be seen in the person who constantly thinks the worst. This catastrophic thinking projects them into a series of alarming but imagined outcomes, fixating on worst-case scenarios. The person who tends to jump to the extreme no matter the size of the problem they are facing. Days for them are either good or bad, black or white. There is little grey area, little balance.

They may be evident in the person who struggles to sleep.

Stress and anxiety might be seen in the person who is in

constant pain, whether there is a medical condition or not. I have five prolapsed discs in my back; some might imagine I should be in pain, but I am not. I used to be in pain when I was anxious, but not anymore.

You might see them in the person who thinks that nobody likes them, convinced that people are talking about them and judging them.

They might be clear in the mother who talks her child out of going away on the school trip and who does this for her sake rather than the child's.

You might see them in the person who says that everything goes wrong for them, that the world has it in for them, who lives in constant victim mode.

Some of us wear it as a badge of honour that we never sit still. I know I did. As a mother of three, I considered my incessant busyness to be part of my role as a mum. I did not realise that I was driven by stress and anxiety, that my need to be constantly on the go was not a choice, it was a compulsion, and it was unhealthy.

These are just some symptoms for you to look out for in your life, in your family, and your friends' lives. Stress and anxiety not only look like the caricature of an anxious person, but they also look like every one of us at times. No exceptions, no immunity.

Anxiety or Caution?

It is important to understand the difference between anxiety and caution. Once we have considered the two, we can establish whether our feelings and our subsequent reactions to those feelings are in proportion or not.

Anxiety has evolutionary benefits. It is wise for an animal to be alert and responsive to potential danger; this ensures survival. A key element of the survival response is that we constantly scan our environment for potential problems. Normally, this ability to scan for threat sits below cognition for the main part. It only bubbles up into our thinking mind when the potential threat changes to a possibility. It goes from something that *could* happen, but *probably won't*, to something that *could* happen and *probably will*, and occasionally to something that *could* happen and *definitely will*. In people with anxiety symptoms, the potential problem rapidly escalates, and they go directly to worst- case scenarios.

So, anxiety is often out of proportion to the perceived threat. That threat may be external, but it is more often an internal feeling. Frequently, the stimulus that has triggered a person is low on the scale of things that should cause concern. Similarly, the habit of constantly projecting into the future, the constant *what-ifs,* and catastrophising exacerbate the problem. When our cognition has been overrun by excessive anxiety the first signs are usually behavioural changes. Anxiety is an avoider, and so initially, you may stop doing the things that normally bring you pleasure. Seeing friends or practising hobbies often become the first casualties of mounting stress and anxiety. This response is counter-intuitive though because these social occasions are the things that help to increase the resilience capacity of our stress bucket.

Caution, on the other hand, is necessary for our survival; it is usually a temporary decision based upon circumstances and fact.

It is a response that is usually in proportion to a threat; it protects us and enables us to make well-thought-out decisions.

Understanding this difference is the first step to identifying when your behaviour is not healthy for you.

I have seen people with genuine reasons to be concerned, but they believe that every precaution they take is a direct result of their anxious mindset. They no longer judge themselves capable of making rational decisions. This is one reason why looking at events in context and perspective is so important.

Michael blamed his anxiety for his reluctance to go out to the pub, which had recently reopened following the Covid-19 lockdown. He was making judgements about his mental health and being critical of himself. Not only this, but he had started to imagine that his colleagues at work were judging him too because they had started to meet up again for a drink after work, and he would not go. His anxiety was based solely on the fact that his colleagues were doing something that he was not, and he put his reasoning not to join them down to anxiety.

I asked him to consider the context. As somebody who had decided to socially distance to protect vulnerable members of his family, why would he go to the pub? He had exercised caution, made a decision based on the facts available to him at the time, and concluded that the best thing for *his* family was to avoid going to the pub with a group of his colleagues.

His anxious mind however, made the judgement that because his decision was at odds with the behaviour of some of his colleagues, that was a further indication of his anxiety. He confused his decision with anxiety rather than seeing it as appropriate caution. This is why we avoid comparing ourselves with other people because we are not using direct factors of comparison. Sometimes, we can just accept that external conditions affect our internal well-being, and it is wise to take precautions.

Other problems arise when people identify with labels, explaining, 'I'm always stressed' or 'I've always been anxious.' Compare this with something like 'There have been times in my life when I have been stressed/anxious.' The latter implies that stress is transitory whilst the former says that stress is a permanent part of who I am, like eye colour. When we describe these emotions as being fundamental parts of us as individuals, problems can arise.

Somebody might say to me that they had a couple of anxious episodes during the week and that is all that they can focus on. After listening to their rundown of events, I will usually say, 'Tell me how long those anxious episodes lasted' and then 'Have you given any thought to the number of anxious episodes that you didn't have in the week?' Maybe the time they spent feeling anxious lasted 20 hours out of 168 hours in a week, which means that this person was not anxious for approximately 88 per cent of that week. When we look at it like this it can help us change perspective because people see that there is so much more to them, and to their lives, than anxiety. When people label themselves as anxious, for much of the time it is often not fact.

Labels often get assigned in childhood: 'Well, you know, she's shy', 'She's timid around new people', 'She's a worrier', and the worst 'She's always been an anxious child'. I cringe when people say to me, 'My mum says I was born anxious', as it always seems like a self-fulfilling prophecy. As adults, we must take responsibility for the information that we give our children. As part of our survival instinct, it is wise to be cautious around people until we feel able to trust them. Caution is not anxiety – it is a sensible precaution. Yet some of these children, who showed reticence around people when they were young, carry the anxiety label for life.

Let's allow our children to grow up without labels because nobody ever pays you a compliment by calling you anxious. In fact, in my opinion, labels of all varieties carry some form of judgement and should be avoided. Instead, let's empower our children, and ourselves, by helping them learn how to trust their own judgement.

Chapter 5

Planning: The What, The Why, and The How

'A goal without a plan is just a wish.'

Antoine de Saint-Exupéry

Often, we take our mental and physical health for granted. Many of us eat what we want, drink what we want, and choose whether we exercise. We also ignore problem thoughts and behaviours that spoil our peace of mind. When we think of the future, one of the things that many of us take for granted is that we will have one. We might not if we follow the path of old patterns and programming because our health might be affected by stress and its hormonal changes. This chapter will help you begin to plan for good health, or if you have already started the journey, to evolve it further.

Planning at the start of a venture is when everything is possible. A good plan focuses us. We can plot key milestones on the journey ahead, and it keeps us accountable. A plan allows us to be creative and consider what we want to achieve at a deeper level, to discover our purpose and how we can achieve it.

Aspirations and intentions aside, we can use the new plan or remodelled map to clarify the changes that we intend to make and identify old, unwanted aspects of our life. One advantage of this type of reflection is that it can bring catharsis, and we can shed any vestige of victimhood as we plan our forward moves.

For planning to be effective, we must consider the past to some extent because it can give us valuable feedback. Looking back can be painful. Many of us have distorted memories of the past to the point where it has become a bogey man. Under the spotlight of worry and rumination, we have amplified its meaning, and not only that, we have discarded better memories.

Imagine if you shine a torch onto something at night, a dog on the path, for example. The torchlight highlights the dog, and everything around it is relegated at best to the shadows and at worst to invisibility in the blackness. If we cannot see something, though, does that mean that it does not exist? No. So, whilst reflective focus is useful, we use it to our advantage and not to add weight to our existing self-limiting stories.

When we decide that certain past experiences will not be repeated, we become alert to old responses, beliefs, thoughts, and behaviours. To prevent history from repeating itself, it is useful to know what it is that we wish to prevent. To avoid *that* happening again in the future, we need to know what *that* is. It is useful to spend some time identifying *that*, to write down how it impacts you and your happiness. Acknowledge what it feels like at its worst and recognise the thoughts, feelings, and sensations that overtake you when held in *that's* grip.

By establishing our pain points we are not wallowing in misery but accepting the existence of barriers which undermine our current mental health. Many of us sweep our problems under the carpet as a coping strategy. This only works in the short term. We also tend to overlook details that do not support our beliefs about the world and our place in it. You see that quite often in relationships, where people focus on what went wrong rather than on what worked. As a species, we default towards the negative bias; the emotional pull towards what went wrong is stronger than what went right. Setting out our pain points signposts the way forward.

Once we acknowledge the pain points, we also have points of reference that mark the progress that we make as we change.

Reference points are important because otherwise we can become disillusioned, thinking that *this* is not working. The human mind's ability to quickly forget how bad things were for us is both an asset and a problem. It is an asset because once we apply changes to our lives, we begin to forget the depth of the problems and the pain they caused, which benefits our recovery. However, on the other hand, ignoring the full extent of the problems often leaves us believing that we have made little progress. When we chart the problem from beginning to end, the improvements we make are clear.

This act of confronting problems, which until now have lurked like the monster under the bed, accepts both their existence and our intention to resolve them. Action is a pillar of resilience. Have you ever been upset with somebody, and perhaps they cannot rectify what happened, but you want them to accept their part? The mind is the same. It is not looking to hold you to account or punish you for the rest of your life. It requires acknowledgement that this is how you feel so that you can accept, set better intentions, and move on.

Having eliminated the things we do not want we can then create a better map. This new map is based on the values that we have which are congruent with who we are now. Large areas of our old map were built on childhood beliefs and experiences which are the old programs to which I often refer. As Aristotle said, 'Give me a child until he is seven, and I will show you the man.' By the time we reach the age of seven, we have clearly established views of the world and our place and worth in it. Have you ever had an argument with someone and told them to stop being childish, or has the accusation of childishness ever been levelled at you? Sometimes people react and you can see the little version of them: trapped, frustrated, and angry at the world. As adults, we think we make decisions for ourselves based on our adult knowledge, but the truth is that adult knowledge and rationale are based on beliefs and assumptions we created in childhood. This childhood programming instilled in us before the age of seven underpins everything.

When we work on mindset, we change old patterns and programming at the deepest level. You would not take financial advice from a seven-year-old. Yet, so many adult decisions that we make are unconscious and based on the reasoning of the child we once were. It is time to bring that childish data up to date so that we can live a life based on current values and knowledge, rather than on an immature and out-of-date theory of the world. We can update our internal software by refreshing these databases from childhood. Now that we are adults, many of us with children of our own, the old code no longer fits.

Our upbringing and experiences are fundamental to the maps that we create. Nobody in the world will have exactly the same maps as you or the same points of reference for the world because nobody has walked it in your shoes, not even your siblings. Many of our most significant maps remain hidden in our unconscious mind, nevertheless they direct the show, existing as background noise rather than overt signposts of who we are and what we believe about ourselves and the world.

Without getting embroiled in politics, Brexit highlighted the power of the maps we each have. I consider myself a good person. I want *good* things for my community, my country, and the world at large. Brexit showed me that people on both sides of the argument consider themselves good people, yet the country was split almost fifty-fifty. Each side has different maps and within those distinct maps are numerous variations in landscape and environment.

Imagine that life is a funnel. Everything that happens draws us to one conclusion. We can choose what we would like that to be, and we can create maps that lead us to it. Too many of us live as though we have few choices. And yet, every day, our choices move us down or away from the funnel. It is unlikely that you would ever hail a taxi without any idea of where you want to go but picture the following scenarios:

Scenario A:

Taxi driver: 'Where to?'

Me: 'Not to Manchester.'

Taxi driver: 'Ok, but where do you want to go?'

Me: 'Definitely not Manchester.'

Some people think that knowing what they do not want is sufficient. They say things like, 'I don't want to feel like this anymore' or 'I don't want to be unhappy.' Avoiding an issue does not make the problem go away; it leaves us constantly looking over our shoulders, waiting for it to return. Moving away from a destination, rather than towards one, means that it is impossible to progress.

If the rationale behind change is what you do not want to put up with anymore, consider the following points. 'I don't want...' can be a good catalyst, an in-the-moment realisation that things must change. However, as a long-term plan, there is no substance to it, and without substance there can be no progress.

Scenario B:

Taxi driver: 'Where to?'

Me: 'Manchester.'

Taxi driver: 'OK.'

Taxi driver: 'OK, we're here, that will be £15 please.'

Me: 'But I wanted Piccadilly Gardens, not the outskirts.'

Taxi driver: 'OK, well, next time be more specific.'

It is good to have a clear idea of where you want to go. However, without some of the finer detail, we risk creating a generic *wish list*. A successful outcome requires precision during the planning phase so that we create the clearest possible vision to work towards.

Sometimes we know where we want to go, but we allow circumstances and minor incidents to sabotage us. This might be an unconscious pattern that crops up frequently, or it might be something that, until now, you have not recognised. Imagine a third scenario. I ask the taxi driver to take me to Piccadilly Gardens because I have an interview at 2 p.m. During the journey I ask him to make a couple of minor diversions, to pick up my dry cleaning and to buy a bottle of water. When I arrive, I am half an hour late and have lost the opportunity to interview. In this scenario, I knew where I wanted to go, but I allowed myself to get distracted from the plan.

I once went for three job interviews in one day. I was thrilled when I got offered all of them. By the end of the day, I managed to turn all three down. On reflection, my anxious mind went into overwhelm. Had I been offered one, I would have accepted it, two I could have considered pros and cons and picked one, but three just sent my mind spinning. An anxious mind avoids, so I turned all three down, hence no problem! Apart from the small fact that I was still unemployed. No plan, no progress.

Planning is the key to successful change; it is both an itinerary and an accountability measure. Even the simplest DIY job, like erecting new shelves, benefits from a plan. You measure the wood (measure twice, cut once according to my partner!), you decide whether to varnish or paint them and how and where to attach them. There is a design process to ensure a reasonable product. It is unlikely that you take a random piece of wood, guesstimate where to cut it, and then find a wall space to hang it. You plan it at some level, even if that plan is just an end picture in your mind. You plan it.

In *The 7 Habits of Highly Effective People*, Steven Covey recommends that we always start with the end in mind. As a teacher, this was a major part of lesson planning. When we start with the end in mind, we have direction, an internal satnav to keep us on route or find acceptable alternatives should we meet a diversion. A satnav is designed to take us to the programmed location, no matter the obstacles, it can adapt to detours, but the destination is firmly set.

Every business has a plan; business loans are contingent on them. Plans are the maps that represent thoughtful strategy. On a home design television programme I watched recently, the architect prepared a 304-page plan for the builder to follow. Plans with this level of detail mean there is less margin for error. With a plan, you have contingencies if any problems arise. We create a plan for mental health goals too. Once our mind has considered the possibilities, recognising both potential difficulties and resolutions, setbacks become less problematic because we already considered them in the planning phase. Often it is the surprise element in events that cause upset and shock. Once we formulate plans, we accept other possibilities may occur and we have a plan B, C, D or E ready.

Many offices have the tradition that people bring cakes to

work on their birthday. Have you ever been the person on a diet when that happened? It is as if all your planning has been undermined, and the diet is under attack. In front of your colleagues, you must decide whether to eat cake or to forgo it. You have a piece, and within your own mind the accusations fly. *You have blown it, all that effort for nothing. You will never lose weight. Oh well, too bad the diet is over now. You might as well have a second piece.* Does this sound familiar? When you read it on the page, does that reaction now seem overblown? One reason to prepare a map is to provide context so that we can appreciate the bigger picture. Just like the satnav, we can accept there will be diversions. Yes, we had a piece of cake, but it is not the end of the world. It only becomes the end of our balanced eating plan if we make that choice and give up. Next time we plan because, after all, the consumption of sweet, sugary snacks seems to be part of the mission statements in many offices. Preparation might involve no longer catastrophising the cake we ate, or we might keep healthier options in our locker. Eating cake is not the end of our diet; our reaction to eating it is what defeats us. Having a plan allows for possibilities, and that means that we are less likely to be hijacked by events, both the expected and the unexpected.

Cakes aside, sometimes the things that we expect to happen do not happen. This can knock us off trajectory. At some level, we believe that our expectations are our due in some way, that we deserve them, and we have the right to be affronted if they do not happen exactly as we hoped. In his book *Are You Ready to Succeed?* Srikumar Rao suggests we avoid becoming over-attached to expectations and remember that resilient people have multiple backup plans. It is such a useful concept because it removes judgement if things do not go our way. Many of us have the notion that *our* way is the only way and that anything else is bad, and that is not necessarily true. Sometimes the best thing for us has never even seemed a possibility. Sometimes, sitting back and waiting to see what happens is best. A friend once explained his understanding of the *Winnie the Pooh* books; although honey tastes good, the pleasure comes in the moments before it is eaten, those moments of anticipation. I wonder what life might be like if we aimed to live in anticipation and appreciation rather than expectation.

As I write this, I am reminded of a trip to Paris made with my three children, at the time aged nine, eleven, and thirteen. When they were small, our contingency plan should they ever find themselves lost was to stop and wait, and I would retrace my steps and find them. We were at the metro, and my two younger children jumped aboard. Before my daughter and I could board, the doors closed, and I watched helplessly as my boys waved at me and the metro moved off. Instant panic! What have I done? What will I say to their father? How will I find them? My daughter turned to me and said, 'What are you getting upset for? Haven't you taught us to stop and wait? They'll get off at the next stop.' She was right; they did. I am forever grateful that they were taught that plan. We do not always have someone to remind us in moments of anxiety, and so we need to learn to do that for ourselves. It is something we will look at in later chapters.

Going back to you, consider what change in your life will look like and what it will feel like. To implement change, we can visualise it, feel it, and link the desire for change to strong emotion to get maximum momentum behind our desire. You are now the author, the artist, the composer of your destiny. Be as bold and as detailed as you can be. There is no right or wrong. Reach for the stars. There is everything to play for. Use metaphors in your design; they are extremely effective. If I say, 'I have a black cloud hanging over me,' you have some idea of what I feel. If you then reassure me with 'There's light at the end of the tunnel,' I know what it is that you want me to understand. The mind loves metaphors. What metaphor would your current experiences have? Does it feel like you have a lead weight on your shoulders? Does it feel like you are walking through treacle? Does it feel like your life is built on quicksand, and no sooner do you feel safe the quicksand moves and you find yourself knee deep again? The mind loves metaphors, so build them into your new design. I feel like a weight has lifted, and I am now floating up light as a feather to grasp my full potential. Try it out for yourself. Ransack the library of your imagination until you find the one that fits, that says it all. The only limit now is one that will be imposed by you.

Once you have the *what* and knowing that we will do the *how* together in this book, you need to consider the *why*?

Considering why you want to change is another important part of the planning process. The stronger the case you can make for embedding change now will strengthen your resolve during the times when you lose focus. Take time to get this right; these are the foundations of your future. If you were building a house, you would not start with the roof. The key to a successful build starts with the foundations. Imagine if the contractor said, 'The budget is insufficient, but if we use poor quality substrate for the foundations, I can bring it in on price.' You would not agree. Working out the foundations for the rest of your life is the most important next step. We get this part right because everything else is supported by it.

Questions that might help you to formulate the *why* might include:

What will be different when I change?

What will that feel like?

Why is this important to me?

Why do I believe that I can do this now?

Why does it matter?

The *how* to embed change will be revealed in more detail as we progress through the book.

Journal Exercise: What Do You Want?

In Chapter 3, we said that resilience requires action. The first act is to write down in a journal or notepad what has brought you to this point in your life and where you want things to change. Having done that, use the *why* questions above to begin to create your blueprint for change. What is it that you do want? If you do not want *that* again, then what do you want? Journals are incredibly useful, and I encourage you to use them. A word of warning, though; used perfunctorily, they become merely a list, but used creatively and honestly, they can become a confidante, a supporter, and your best accountability partner.

Sit down, prepare yourself, and write down exactly what it is like for you at this moment in time. A kiss-and-tell book of your life but for your consumption only. You never have to share it or let anybody else read it, but this is the start of developing resilience. Getting points down on paper makes the process clearer. Keep focusing on the detail to get exactly what you want from the plan. Once everything is recorded, we have a reference point; we shine a light on past experiences lurking in the shadows, the monsters under the bed whispering old propaganda but never coming boldly out into the light and identifying themselves. Until now.

Once we establish our plan, we reduce the possibility of rogue surprises, we expect things to arise, and we are prepared. We are packing a toolbox that will be filled with Resilience Template™ tools. There is a saying, 'Fail to plan, plan to fail', and it is equally apt when embarking on a journey to improve our mental health. Keep tight hold of the map and be the person who is never knowingly underprepared. When it comes to your mental health, it will pay dividends.

Chapter 6

The Resilience Template – 7 Steps to Improve Your Mental Health

'The Magical Number Seven, Plus or Minus Two: Some Limits on Our Capacity for Processing Information.'

George A. Miller

I believe that in the 21st century we deserve better understanding of mental health and what we personally can do to improve and maintain it. For this reason I am excited to share The Resilience Template™ because I have seen it transform lives. The process has seven steps: each step builds on the previous one. It is important not to race ahead, no matter how eager you feel, because all the steps are needed to provide a framework to create change. If we move ahead too quickly, before we have embedded each one, we risk undermining the foundations. Expect to be a tortoise rather than a hare and implement changes steadily and repeatedly. This is the only way to build real, lifelong transformation.

So, the term 'seven steps' does not equate to seven days or even seven weeks. There is no fixed time limit, and it does not suggest a quick fix. Such a thing does not exist when dealing with mental health. Each step will awaken different challenges for people. There is no one size fits all when it comes to the most important asset that we have: the mind. The Resilience Template™ is a guide for you to use and one that you can refer to frequently. As you familiarise yourself with the exercises, your mind will become clearer, and the decisions that you make will fall in line with your values. As your awareness expands, you will find more ways to apply the exercises in your daily routine. Just as The Resilience Template™ framework underpins the process of change, good mental health underpins the quality of our life. Without peace of mind, life is built on quicksand.

There is no 'end by' date when it comes to having a healthy mindset. As with any resource after acquisition comes maintenance, and that requires commitment, consistency, and diligence. If it sounds like hard work, it is ... and it isn't, because everything is easier when you are not hijacked by outdated beliefs and habits.

At a training event I attended recently the attendees were asked to write down the seven steps to make a good cup of tea. Mine are as follows:

1. Boil water in the kettle

2. Put a teabag in a cup
3. Pour on hot water
4. Leave to steep
5. Remove the teabag
6. Add milk
7. Stir.

It is interesting to break things down because sometimes we forget the complexity of even the most mundane tasks. Look again at the list, what happens if I miss out any of the steps? Omitting any one of them will affect the quality of my cup of tea. Likewise, there are no short cuts to good mental health. Think marathon training, think daily commitment, think transformation.

In the 1950s, researchers found that short-term memory, our conscious mind, can only remember between five and nine facts or tasks; the ideal number is seven. They called it the 'magical number seven'; it is why landline telephone numbers used to have maximum seven numbers. We can describe conscious working memory as a chalkboard, on which we scrawl snippets of information. In contrast, the subconscious mind is a vast library of life's data and experience.

Staying with the 'magical number seven', The Resilience Template™ also has seven PARTNER steps, and, like making a good cup of tea, all are essential.

1. **Preparation**
2. **Acceptance**
3. **Reconnection**
4. **Talk to Self**
5. **Now**

6. **E**mbed – Practice and Diligence
7. **R**outine – Create a Routine to Hang it On

The PARTNER steps, which are the framework for The Resilience Template™, remind us that success depends on an effective partnership between the conscious and subconscious mind.

The conscious mind is everything within our awareness, where we make conscious choices and decisions about our life: where to live, what to wear, what to eat, and so on. It contains the thoughts, memories, and feelings which currently sit in our awareness. Our conscious mind can hold on average seven conscious thoughts at any one time, but researchers estimate that we have between 6,000 and 50,000 thoughts a day. The rest of them float around the subconscious mind, which is a database of all the experiences we have ever had, every thought, emotion, and feeling. Whilst the conscious mind has a very short-term memory, the subconscious memory store is infinite. It is a vast library of your life to date.

The subconscious mind is twenty times more powerful than its conscious counterpart. It has the ruling voice, the controlling vote, much of the time. You might see the relationship between the two play out in the self-talk of the woman who wants to lose weight,

'I think I can lose the weight this time, but I have failed so many diets before. I just don't seem to have the willpower my friends have.'

As soon as I hear the word *but,* I look for the subconscious mind at work. Onboard and working with us, it is a powerhouse.

But when it is working against us, when it applies outdated experience and beliefs to a current situation and sees only failure, then it will likely undermine us. If we want to embed effective change in the shortest time frame, we work with the subconscious mind. As a therapist, I draw from some of the core therapy practices which work directly with the subconscious, including Clinical Hypnotherapy and the Emotional Freedom Technique (EFT), to drive change. The Resilience Template™ techniques will support you as you retrain the old mind so that it no longer flits from thought to thought, and from internal drama to internal drama.

When we get both mind partners working together towards the same goals, we have a great dynamo for change.

The resilient part of you understands that you are a work in progress, and that means that you are prepared for both good and less-good days. The Resilience Template™ exercises will help you to use the less-good days as feedback. It will be easier to accept them because you planned for them, and so you will no longer fight against them. Instead, you will be flexible, bending, not breaking. You will tune in to your own needs, and you will learn how to acknowledge your needs. Preparing for the good times is as important as preparing for the difficult, and The Resilience Template™ will provide support as you develop a new set of priorities that are compatible with the person you are today.

Be consistent, take the rough with the smooth, and be prepared. You've got this!

Chapter 7

❧

P is for Preparation

'Give me six hours to chop down a tree and I will spend the first four sharpening the axe.'

Abraham Lincoln

Imagine if I walked into the living room, intending to redecorate, and found the room was on fire. In theory, I have two choices: extinguish the fire or begin the decorating. I could say that I will put the fire out when I have finished decorating as planned, but I am setting myself up to fail. The sensible thing to do is to extinguish the fire. Once the fire is extinguished, then I assess the damage and decide how to reclaim the room. It is counterproductive to move ahead of this stage because without a safe environment in which to work we cannot improve our current situation.

This first step in The Resilience Template™ extinguishes the fire and calms the nervous system, preparing the foundations for the transformative work ahead. As we progress we will add new steps and structure to the process. The better we prepare, the easier it will be to embed changes. During preparation, as we calm the nervous system, we disengage the fight or flight response and begin to feel safe. We slow down our heart rate, increase oxygen intake, change focus, and develop a sense of grounding. Expect to spend a minimum of twenty-one days calming your nervous system, practising the techniques, and settling internal turmoil.

Every gardener knows the importance of ground preparation before planting. We remove any weeds, aerate the ground, and add nutrients to the soil to protect the vulnerable seedlings. We too need to devote preparation time because once we decide to change, many of us are eager to move forward and we risk our success if we do so too quickly. This phase of our transformation is delicate. We have decided to change but are still not entirely convinced that it is possible or even within our capability. These concerns, along with unfamiliar and close introspection, make us vulnerable, so we work slowly and diligently.

Journal Exercise: Do You Feel Safe?

Some of us will have little memory of ever feeling safe. Learning what safety means to you personally is important. Use the following questions as a guide to help you assess how safe you currently feel:

Do you sleep well?

Do you feel settled?

Do you tend to overstretch yourself and take on too much?

Do you demand perfection of yourself at all times?

Do you choose to spend time relaxing?

Do you feel that others judge you?

Feelings of safety keep us grounded. If grounding is being rooted like an oak, then being ungrounded is a kite constantly whipped up by the wind, never settling or resting, always pushed on by an unseen force. Our roots provide strength, and they anchor us. They allow us to be buffeted like trees in the wind. We bend but do not break, but without roots we flit from one thing to the next, unable to settle, insecure and always second-guessing our decisions. Our self-worth decreases, and we become convinced of our inability to cope. We spend our lives criticising our self-perceived faults, our lack, our right even to be here.

The most familiar grounding techniques anchor the breath. They are effective and can be learned quickly. Deep breathing calms the nervous system, providing a manual override to the fight or flight reaction. When breathing is relaxed, oxygen and carbon dioxide are balanced in our bodies. The heart rate slows down, and the symptoms of stress and anxiety subside. Relaxed breathing can prevent stress from accruing in our buckets.

During the fight or flight reaction, our breathing becomes shallow and rapid. This is because to 'fight' or 'flee', we need to ready our body for action. We can regain calm by focusing on the breath. This acts as a manual override, a conscious instruction to the brain, and a command to the automated stress response to stand down because there is no threat.

It is easy to underestimate the importance of good breathing; after all, we breathe all the time, a fact that many of us take for granted. The act of breathing itself does not guarantee the quality of our breathing. This is simply because many of us have developed the habit of shallow breathing. Poor quality breathing inhibits oxygen intake, which we need to fuel healthy cells. Every function in our body, including digestion, muscle movement, and thinking, relies on ample supplies of oxygen. Without sufficient oxygen, we risk impairing these vital processes.

The good news is that poor breathing habits can be unlearnt and through training we can develop better ones. The intention in learning new breathing techniques is not to breathe in these ways all the time. It is to break the poor breathing patterns you may have established. Just like exercises that you do at the gym to retrain muscle memory, such exercises may feel uncomfortable at first. Persevere with the exercises in this chapter for at least 21 days before adding in the exercises in the next chapters. This will give you the opportunity to establish good foundations on which to build the subsequent mental resilience techniques.

As you practise the breathing techniques add conscious instruction statements. As you breathe in, say to yourself 'calm' and as you exhale, say 'letting go.' These verbal instructions direct the mind to override the stress response too, accepting the possibility of calm and releasing the saboteurs of anxiety and stress. I have recorded the exercises on the website.

Preparation Technique: 4-2-7 Breathing

Here is a simple, effective breathing exercise called 4-2-7. Practise it several times a day, every hour if possible, and continue to do it over a period of at least twenty-one days. Later in the book, we will create a daily routine of which this will be one element but, in the meantime, practise until it becomes familiar and natural.

Breathe in through your nose for a count of four, hold it for a count of two, and release through your mouth for a count of seven.

As you breathe in, your abdomen expands, as if you have a balloon inside. As you slowly exhale through your mouth, your heart rate will start to slow down.

Breathing in for a count of four, say to yourself, 'calm.' Hold for a count of two, and as you breathe out, remind yourself to 'let go' as you count to seven.

If it feels comfortable to do so close your eyes, conjuring up images of calm. If you are unable to create mental images, then with your eyes closed, focus on the breath, and continue to give the verbal instruction 'calm.'

Take five or six breaths in this way. Once you have slowed everything down, you can let your breathing settle.

Sit quietly for a few moments afterwards. Then come back into your environment with a smile, knowing that you have taken a few minutes out of your day to establish calm.

Preparation Technique: Square Breathing

With a straight back and relaxed body, let your hands hang by your side (if sitting, let your hands rest on your thighs).

Count to four in your head as you breathe in through your nose, hold for a count of four, breathe out through your mouth for a count of four and hold for a count of four.

If it feels comfortable to do so, then close your eyes.

Add the verbal instructions to be calm and to let go of stress.

Breathe in this way for five or six breaths.

Sit quietly and notice how you feel.

Remember, the aim is not to breathe in this manner all the time; it is to retrain the old muscle memory, which has led to shallow breathing.

Preparation Technique: 3-2-1 Reset

When we get stuck in a loop of anxiety, we can break the loop by stimulating the brain bilaterally. Dr Richard K. Nongard, Hypnotherapist and Trainer describes this technique as a self-hypnosis resource to instill calm and resilience. It is also, a havening technique which is a psychosensory therapy; we apply a sensory touch to produce a calming response in the brain. This generates delta brainwaves which normally are only produced during sleep and which are themselves soothing and calming. This technique is deceptively simple but effective. It can be challenging because it requires some self-kindness, and this may feel difficult if you think negatively about yourself. There is a recording on the website as well. Set two minutes on a timer. Then with eyes open:

Take *three* deep belly breaths. You can use the 4-2-7 Breathing technique here or any other that you find effective.

Cross your *two* arms over your chest, placing your hands on opposite shoulders, and close your eyes if it feels comfortable to do so. Slowly begin to slide your hands from your shoulders down to your elbows. Up and down, up and down. Repeat the words 'I am safe.'

Do this for *one* minute or until the timer ends.

Do this technique every time you wash your hands; in this way, you will practise it many times a day. If it feels strange to do this, remember that when comforting other people, we often rub them reassuringly, up and down their arms. We are merely transferring this reassurance to ourselves.

The technique above soothes our internal environment, calming the nervous system but there are other things we can do because sometimes it feels as though we have no control. We do. In our immediate environment, for example, we are in control of what we eat, drink, and the exercise that we do. These are things to consider consciously because they will all help you to create a healthy internal environment.

Additionally, it is worth considering how much time you spend watching television or using social media. These often promote the negative sides of life because the media know that they increase viewing figures. Our home is our haven, yet, throughout the day, we allow the television channels to invade it. If you are experiencing stress and anxiety, limiting your exposure to programmes like the news is a good idea.

Even soap operas entertain us with disturbing plots. At a time when you might hope for television programmes to lift your spirit, the storylines of dying babies and psychotic madmen add to the national misery. There is a serious point to this because our unconscious mind does not differentiate between fact and fiction. Have you ever cried at a film? If the answer is yes that indicates that at some level, your mind does not recognise this as fiction but as part of your reality, as an event currently happening in your life. Hence your reaction.

The mind absorbs the information on television or radio, seen with our own eyes or heard with our own ears, and thinks it is happening to us. Does this go some way to understanding why our stress bucket is full? The doom and gloom, the multiple traumas in one television episode, are detrimental to our mental health. If you can, choose light entertainment programmes, listen to your favourite CDs and dance around the kitchen. Be playful, do things that make you laugh and smile, things that expand your stress bucket but don't get sucked into the daily media misery fest. If you don't want to give up watching the news or the gritty crime drama you enjoy, then make sure that you are receiving an equal balance of positive input so that your brain isn't just exposed to continuously negative propaganda.

Even without sitting down to deliberately watch a programme, many of us have the television or radio on in the background. When you are feeling vulnerable, I'd recommend either turning it off or being more selective about the programmes you choose. It is unhealthy to be constantly force-fed bad news, and as we absorb it subliminally, we do not even realise how much it affects us. Consider our ancestors living in a world pre-television, and telephone. They did not have real-time access to what was going on in the next town, never mind across the world. In fact, they often will not have known what was happening beyond their own immediate sphere. Nowadays, with technology at our fingertips, whilst it is important that we remain informed, sometimes it is necessary to switch off and focus on our own mental health. Please make conscious choices about the programmes that you watch. Ask yourself 'Will this uplift me or add to my personal worry?' Then make the best decision for you.

Many of us feel compelled to respond immediately if our mobile phone pings or we get caught up in social media sites that often undermine our sense of well-being, and these can become personal timewasters. Limiting your time online will free up time to practise the techniques, but also it will give you a break from constant external, unfiltered input.

In the Abraham Lincoln quotation at the start of this chapter, we stress the importance of preparation. It is the key to embedding good habits. First, we calm the nervous system and prepare the ground. We work at this level until we feel grounded and safe, enjoying the journey for what it is and accepting that there is no quick fix.

Journal Exercise: Check-in

After 21 days of preparation, assess your progress. Have you noticed a change in how you react to problems? Have you seen an improvement in your focus? Do you feel ready to move on? Or is there still work to do at this level? As you move forward, continue using these tools every day. It is important to keep your stress level dampened down.

For a selection of PDF, audio and video resources, visit www.resiliencetemplate.com

Chapter 8

❦

A is for Acceptance

'We cannot change anything until we accept it. Condemnation does not liberate, it oppresses.'

Carl Jung

The story that we tell ourselves, that we repeat to ourselves and others, becomes the story we live every day. Many of us get stuck in the quicksand of past stories. The thing is, we all have had times that we thought would break us, but the fact that we are still here shows that they did not. Acceptance means accepting what has gone before without attempting to fight it, judge it, or resist it.

Resistance is the antithesis of acceptance, and it keeps the story alive and fresh in our minds. It means that we do not give ourselves the opportunity to put our past behind us so that we can heal. It often leads to bitterness and anger, both of which gnaw at us.

From the moment of conception, both good and bad things will happen. Some of us will be born to incapable parents. Some of us will be put at risk. Some of us will grow up feeling belittled and unloved. Some of us will experience turmoil and pain. Some of us will form unhealthy relationships. Some of us will live in fear daily. Some of us will look at others and be envious of their lives. Some of us will have these experiences, and more besides, it is not right or just or fair, but it is a fact.

And yet, despite the pain, the human spirit can soar. Out of sorrow and misery can come amazing stories of resilience, and of successful lives which reflect the great capacity that we each have for transformation and joy. We can learn to fly again. We can find our true voice, growing from a whisper to a shout until we become the best version of ourselves, and then we get the opportunity to sing the expression of our soul to the universe.

But we can only do this when we recognise that if we want to see change in our lives, then we must be the ones to change. Then we accept the past and stop the blame game, no matter how justified we feel. We can then focus on how to move forward. If not, we let the old stories underscore our lives and we dance to the beat of old pain, misery, and mistakes, and it is a tired history that has little, if any, relevance to the people we are today.

Constant repetition of painful past experiences reinforces the narrative, constructing and embedding neural pathways in our brains and preventing us from moving beyond 'the story'. Sadly, many of us become 'the story'. It does not improve things, but it does keep the negative narrative alive. The practice of acceptance consigns the story to the past so that we no longer relive it, and we no longer are the ones responsible for allowing it to affect the present and the future.

The rear-view mirror in a car makes objects appear closer than they are. It is the same in our lives because much of the stuff that affects us, is now behind us. It happened to us a long time ago. Only one person is responsible for the repeat performances in our minds. It is up to us to change to a more uplifting channel.

This may seem like a harsh question, but how many of us return to the story again and again either because we cannot let it go or to justify the current decisions we make? We pick the scab, and we interrupt our healing. Every time we return to old history, to negative stories from the past, we hurt ourselves.

Journal Exercise: Addressing the Unacceptable

Using your journal, take some time to recall the things or experiences that, up until now, you have felt unable to accept. Once you have a list, then reflect, what do you gain by holding on? How can you let this go? Acceptance does not seek to diminish what you have been through, but it does draw a line. If the process of acceptance causes you intense pain, seeing a therapist might be a necessary step forward.

Acceptance does not mean resignation to more suffering; it means that you acknowledge that an experience happened, that it caused pain, and that, sadly, there is nothing you can do to change that. It does not mean that it was okay that it happened. It is simply an acknowledgement that it did. Acceptance provides a base from which you can move on.

Acceptance brings with it the realisation that we have sole responsibility for our well-being. We can influence other people's happiness levels, but ultimately the only life we can change is our own. This knowledge is empowering. Even if somebody has hurt you previously, they can only continue to impact your life if you allow it.

Each of us has our wounds from the past. Even siblings often have different experiences growing up in the same home. All pain hurts. Whether you have experienced what the experts call *capital T Trauma* or *small t trauma,* your pain matters; nobody can call 'Top Trumps' on it.

When we accept, we acknowledge our pain with compassion, and we liberate ourselves to a kinder future. By the time I reached 50, I had seen too many people that I loved die. I saw such a waste of opportunity, lives lost to bitterness and anger. It is so much more productive to focus on what, or who, you have in your life rather than on what, or who, you have lost or on what has been taken from you. No joy comes from anger or bitterness about what has gone before.

Have you ever bought a new car, and suddenly it seemed like everyone in town was driving the same model? Our mind sees what it expects to see, and it feels what it expects to feel. We get more of what we focus on. This is an important reason to accept and move on because to experience a better life, the images we play in our minds must be relevant to who we are now. Instead of negating our experiences, acceptance becomes the wisdom with which we transform our lives. There is a reason that a vehicle's windscreen is bigger than the rear-view mirror; it is more important to see where we are going. Looking back might give us useful feedback, but it is the road ahead that gets us to our destination. Acceptance of the past is not the end of our problems, but it goes a long way towards helping us live healthier lives.

Acceptance of the present and the challenges we face is also fundamental to our well-being. As I said earlier in the chapter, we are not all equally blessed, but we can all accept our blessings equally. Acceptance provides us with an opportunity to focus on what we have, shifting the focus away from what we do not have. We live in a culture with a great emphasis on physical appearance. We see unhappy people changing their faces and bodies because they hope they will feel better internally by changing themselves externally. It is not unreasonable to want to look nice, but when that becomes your life's total focus, you are feeding a potential monster who may never be satisfied.

As I write this, I am mindful of the story of the black dog and the white dog as told by John R. Bisagno in *The Power of Positive Praying* (1965):

> An old missionary returned to the home of a convert among the Mohave Indians. When the missionary asked him how he was doing, old Joe said, 'Well, it seems that I have a black dog and a white dog inside of me and they are always fighting.' The missionary asked him, 'Which one wins?' and Joe said, 'The one I feed the most.'

Let resilience and acceptance be the white dog which we

nourish, train, and exercise. Through acceptance, we accept the parts of ourselves that we may not like and cannot change. Accepting who we are saves energy for the important things in life because internal conflict is exhausting. It is a 24/7 battle, and if the struggle is self-fought, we can never win.

We can also learn to accept other aspects of ourselves, like our susceptibility to anxiety and stress. From a calmer place, a place where we no longer fight with old ghosts and old fears, we no longer respond with fear when they reappear. They are familiar acquaintances, possibly unwanted guests gate-crashing our party of life, but that is all. We acknowledge their existence but refuse to get drawn into conflict, recognising them as physiological responses. We accept, and the fighting within stops.

Otherwise, when we try to push them away, when we try to ignore them, they spring back like a jack-in-the-box. Instead we accept that stress and anxiety exist as physiological responses, and we give them no more meaning than we give a sneeze. Once we use the preparation techniques to calm the nervous system, anxiety will appear less often, and its reappearance will no longer take us by surprise or derail us.

In developing the four pillars of resilience, we accept the reality of anxiety and stress, and we manage them better. Retraining our minds to accept that sometimes we will get stressed and anxious, but we have plans and strategies in place, and that knowledge liberates us from the fear we may once have associated with these feelings.

Accept the emotions that can and will come up for you. They

are not your enemy; it is your reaction to them that causes you pain. It is okay to feel sad, it is okay to feel angry, it is okay to feel worried. It is also okay to feel happy, excited, and joyful. Whether we judge them good or bad we do not have to push our emotions away. Think of them as a warning light appearing on your car dashboard – they may be indicators of something more serious but often they are transient issues. Accept that some days you will feel sad and you might not know why and, on those days, say to yourself, 'it is just another rainbow day.' Some days you feel blue and some days you feel sunshine yellow, and in between are a whole range of colourful emotions. You can accept them all. Think of an artist with a palette of colours which he mixes to add depth and context to his paintings. We have a palette of emotions which create light and shade in our life. If we were not meant to experience the full spectrum over time, why have them? Accept the full experience and stop fighting them or judging them. Allow yourself a bad day now and again, and when it comes be kind to yourself. So, the emotions that we experience are not the problem, our problems come when we fight them or get stuck in them. If you can, learn to accept them as natural aspects of being human. Nothing more.

Accept too that anxiety is an avoider; it stops you from getting on with your life. Have you noticed that when you are feeling anxious, you stop going out? You stop seeing friends. You stop doing the things that make you smile. I wonder what would happen if, instead of caving in, you did what you had planned to do anyway. The best response to anxiety is to do just that and say, 'Join me if you must, but I have things that I plan to do, so you can fit in around me.' No longer under the spotlight, consuming your attention and energy, anxiety will slowly melt away because as you focus on doing other things, it has no place there.

Remember, too, that tiredness and an unhealthy diet are breeding grounds for anxiety. Some days you will be tired, and, on those days, it is okay to accept that you are probably not going to achieve what you had planned. At these times, schedule in some early nights and reward yourself with some time off. You will come back more energised and refreshed.

Similarly, just as there will be days when you are too tired, there may be days when you do not eat nutritiously. As often as you can, ensure that your food choices are appropriate and will provide maximum sustenance. If you find yourself continually struggling to choose nourishing foods when you feel anxious or off-balance emotionally, then meal preparation can be a good way of combatting this. Think back to the maps we discussed earlier. Food planning and preparation are significant parts of the detail in the map of healthy eating. You might decide to prepare balanced meals on Sunday for the week ahead, thus taking some of the pressure off. Then if you have a busy day, you will not be tempted to eat poorly because you already have a pre-prepared balanced meal, which is an easy, ready-made option.

Acceptance Technique: The Soothing Tap

This is a great technique to use when you want to slip into relaxation. It soothes the stress response. It is also a good hand position to use during any meditation or visualisation experience. I have recorded an audio, on the website, to help you find the right finger/hand position.

Place the hand to be tapped, palm down, over the centre of your chest.

With the fingers of your other hand, locate the valley between the ring finger and little finger, above the knuckle toward the wrist. You can place your thumb on the palm of the hand you are tapping to anchor the fingers. Push and release or tap firmly, about ten times, breathing deeply.

This can be used with any mediation or relaxation recording.

If using it as a mode to accept what has happened previously, say, 'Even though [xxx] happened, I accept that it happened, and I love and accept myself anyway.' Repeat twice more.

Pause and take a deep breath.

Continue to tap a further twenty times.

Pause again. Take a deep breath and notice what comes up for you.

Continue to tap for as long as it feels comfortable, stopping regularly to tune in and notice what feelings and thoughts arise for you.

Repeat, switching hands.

Go back to the list that you made of the things that you cannot accept and tap through each one. Continue until you feel calmer about each situation before moving onto the next. Some things will be easier to accept than others. That is fine. We are not in a race. We continue until we have resolution and peace of mind.

Acceptance Technique: Can You Change It?

Another way to accept the things that have happened is to ask yourself, 'Can I change them?' If not, then learning to accept them is fundamental. Remember that pragmatism and action are two of the four pillars of resilience. No matter how painful, if there is no retrospective action that I can take to change what happened, then I am only hurting myself by constantly recalling events.

Acceptance can be difficult for us to go through, especially if we have spent a long time entangled in the past. If you do find this difficult, then please consider seeing a therapist.

For resources, visit www.resiliencetemplate.com

Chapter 9

R is for Reconnect

*'Sometimes we have to disconnect in order to
reconnect with what matters.'*

Unknown

When we reconnect with ourselves, we learn how to love ourselves. We get back to the basics, no longer criticising ourselves for every mistake we have ever made; we choose to be kinder to ourselves. We see beyond our human flaws, our failures, our appearance, and the faults that we perceive. We accept who we are, how far we have come, and we stop the negative internal commentary. To reconnect, we must first disconnect old anchors to the past, limiting beliefs, unhelpful thinking, and behaviours that are detrimental to our peace of mind. We do this by bringing our conscious awareness into the present moment and challenging thoughts that previously slipped by, as we were functioning primarily on autopilot. We develop mindfulness.

I am reminded of Kelly who had experienced significant abuse as a teenager. She felt that she could not move forward, and she lived very much in the past, in some part due to the guilt that she continued to carry. If you cannot move forward and if you cannot change the past, then you become trapped in a place of painful retrospection. We considered the following scenario to help her see the damage that her grip on the past was causing her:

Imagine you bring a cheap bottle of wine to a party. Upon arrival, you pour yourself a glass. When you taste it, you realise that it is horrible, and you wish that you had bought a better quality bottle. You look around, worried that others may have noticed your predicament. Embarrassment and fear of judgement arise in you. Perhaps, childhood stories of people worse off than you remind you that it is wasteful to throw things away. Maybe your immediate response is that you made your bed and should suffer for it. You keep hold of the glass and, whilst you cannot enjoy it, you pretend to take the odd sip. The host comes round with a lovely bottle of something grand, filling up the guests' glasses. He either skips you because he assumes you have a full glass, or you decline because you are embarrassed. Either way, everybody gets to enjoy their lovely wine whilst you sit quietly in the corner stewing in a myriad of emotions and self-recriminations and missing out. Sometimes, we choose to get rid of the old to make room for something better, no matter how much it goes against our programming.

Disconnecting from our old ways requires self-awareness. When we remove something that has been present for a long time, it inevitably leaves an imprint or void. We have been so used to it taking up space in our minds that we need a replacement.

If issues are holding you back, you will have formed habits around them. These will have created neural pathways in your mind, and because these habits have been built over time, they have developed muscles that will not suddenly disappear. They may be habits of feeling guilty, habits of poor self-talk, habits of aggressive behaviour, or they may be something entirely different.

Imagine being at the beach, and you dig a big hole in the sand. If you leave the hole without filling it with something solid, like pebbles, the sea will wash over it, bringing more sand, and the hole will fill again. It will be no different from when you first started to dig. To sustain change, we find healthy alternatives. We make better choices to prevent the void from refilling with old beliefs and behaviours. Do not leave the vacuum empty because it will refill.

Reconnection allows us to prioritise our needs. Many of us, particularly the anxious people-pleasers amongst us, stay quiet, always conceding to other people. We follow other people's whims for an easier life, although it does not always work out like that, and in doing so, we often find ourselves inwardly resentful. This suppression of our own preferences and needs, when perpetuated long-term, is unhealthy at a mental and physical level.

People-pleasers often began life as parent-pleasers, and many of us have run this programmed pattern for a long time. Speak your truth honestly and clearly but get into the habit of speaking it because suppression builds stress and accumulated over time that causes damage.

Mothers often put their children's needs before their own, and with young children, that is understandable. However, as our children become more independent, the balance should begin to tip again in our favour. Putting aside whether you are the parent of somebody, the partner, the child, the friend, or the employee, you are a human being with your own needs. Consider the safety instructions on airplanes: in case of emergency, put on your own lifejacket first, or administer your own oxygen, and then help others. It is not a selfish arbitrary instruction but a sensible response in a difficult situation.

Every human being has needs: the need to feel safe, to have food and water, to have time to relax and grow, and to have dreams and aspirations. Never negate your own needs, because there is nobody on this earth who is more important than you are. Once you accept this, once you see your value, you permit yourself to reconnect and plan for your own needs. Planning is one of the pillars of resilience. This is a good opportunity for you to explore aspirations that have taken a back seat in your list of priorities.

Many people drive nice cars, and I have witnessed many treat their cars better than they treat themselves. Reconnection ensures that we take time to check in and listen to what our body needs–refuelling and doing the things that replenish us.

As we tune in to the current version of ourselves, our old beliefs become less dogmatic. We change some of our old filters of perception and begin to see the world through fresh eyes; this is priceless. For too long, many of us have been limited by childhood assumptions and poor self-belief. No longer will we sell ourselves short; we will no longer miss out on opportunities because we will no longer allow these outdated beliefs to undermine us. Now we break free of constrictions that limit us. As adults, we draw a line in the sand. We throw away the bitter wine in our glass so that we can drink from the cup of self-kindness.

Disconnection and reconnection are not necessarily linear processes. They can happen in parallel and over time. Sometimes, we bring in a new idea, replacing an old one. At other times, we decide we no longer want to continue an existing habit, and we consider better alternatives. Over a period, we replace the old with the new.

This process does not only improve our mental health, it provides us with a measure of our internal dialogue, and it also makes us more self-aware physically. We begin to notice more closely what is happening internally and externally. When we tune in to our bodies, we notice aches and pains before they become larger problems. I have several prolapsed spinal discs, and that damage did not happen to me overnight. It happened over time, but I was too caught up in an anxious head, too distracted by minor worries, that I missed the early signs. I am not unusual. Many of us ignore the warnings because we are so enmeshed in insignificant *problems*. Problems that are certainly not worth risking our health for.

I was absent from work with the pain of prolapsed discs in

my lumbar region and saw a doctor from the Occupational Health Unit who criticised me for walking with a limp. He told me that I had 'absolutely no mechanical problem with my back' and that I should walk about as normal because the pain was in my head. I was four days away from having an MRI scan, which would have shown the problem, but at his insistence, I ignored the pain, and I walked through it. Within the hour, I collapsed in agony and spent the next month on complete bed rest. Although I blamed that doctor for a long time, the fault was mine. I knew that the pain was real, but I did not trust my connection with my body. I could have ignored his diagnosis, but my anxiety symptoms and guilt about my work absence meant that I placed more trust in him than in myself. This taught me such an important lesson, though it cost me greatly at the time. I learned to rebuild and trust my own connection with my body. The situation was similar when I was struggling with chronic insomnia. Once I stepped back and took back responsibility from the medical profession, I discovered solutions. These did not appear instantly; instead, over time, I reconnected and tuned into my own body. I developed trust in myself and I listened to what my body was telling me.

Self-trust can be a big ask for those of us who may have grown up not even liking ourselves, in which case we struggle to want the best for ourselves or even to acknowledge that we deserve the best. We tend to only look after the things and people that we care about. If that does not include us, then, of course, it is natural to neglect ourselves and put other people and their opinions ahead of our own.

Imagine that you are on your way to an interview for your dream job, and your friend calls and persuades you to call in on her on the way. By compromising the time available, you could make yourself late for the interview. Your opportunity to calmly prepare could also be affected. Potentially you could jeopardise your chances of getting the job. No matter our friend's needs, we can never neglect our own. Sometimes there are inevitable diversions to affect our plans. Some will be opportunities, and others will be distractions, and it is not always easy to spot the difference but focusing on our own needs rather than on constantly pleasing others will keep us on track.

Planning is an important tenet in self-care, and reconnection is an integral part of the plan. It provides us with information on what is happening below the surface. It helps us to recalibrate and brings our focus to a higher level where we assess what we need to do to achieve peak performance. In this way we plan our day so that our actions support our mental resilience. In Chapter 12, we consider how to adapt our existing schedule to integrate the tools that will help us do this.

Another important part of reconnection is discovering what matters most, and that includes our values. When *life* is happening, whether good or bad, our values keep us heading in the right direction. They keep us on track and able to manage diversions and detours.

Journal Exercise: Values

In your journal, write down the top five values that you currently have. Here are some areas of your life to consider: family, career, health, education, relationships, wealth, and travel. What do you value most? Is it independence? Is it security? Is it compassion? Values are not to be confused with emotions which are transitory and change frequently. Consider traits like;

competence, honesty, loyalty, reliability, responsibleness, success, and trustworthiness. There are so many values for you to consider, and over time, some will change as your circumstances change. When you know your values, you can use them to assess the usefulness of any decision that you are about to make. Ask yourself:

Will what I am about to do or say, move me forward?

Will what I am about to do or say, sit comfortably with my values?

Will this reaction bring me peace of mind?

When we act against our values, it causes internal conflict and unease. Some call that the voice of conscience or guilt, the voice that niggles away at you. It consumes your energy, diverts you from your goals, and turns the fight inwards. But when we use our values as our benchmark, we take time to reflect, pause, gain clarity and certainty, and make better decisions because they are consistent with the best version of ourselves. We are not the magpie flying from one shiny thing to the next. We become proactive and not reactive.

Reconnection Technique: Five, Four, Three, Two, One

Practise this exercise whenever you have a few moments to spare and then have it ready to use when you feel anxiety building. The audio recording is on the website.

Look around you and find:

Five things you can see. Focus on each before moving on.

Four things you can touch. Focus on each before moving on.

Three things you can hear. Focus on each before moving on.

Two things you can smell. Focus on each before moving on.

One thing you can taste. Focus on it a moment.

This technique can help when you feel as though random emotions are ambushing you. Experiment with it, use it inside or outdoors, in the car, or walking the dog. We engage the senses, which helps us reconnect with our bodies, and it helps as we connect with our immediate environment. We stay in the moment. When we are anxious, we tend to fear future possibilities, worrying about what may happen or about the past and what has already happened. The only place that we can have some control is the present. Reconnection and grounding help us to stay present.

Reconnection Technique: Gratitude

Focusing on gratitude is an excellent way to reconnect and fill the void left by old habits of thinking.

As you wake each morning and as you begin to fall asleep, you naturally go through trance-like states which makes these times of day ideal for practising gratitude.

Choose three things to be grateful for and make one always about you. Consider how grateful you are for each of them. They do not have to be big things. We have so many things, small and large, to be grateful for, and it can be humbling to choose, especially for those of us who often get caught in a negative loop of focusing on what we do not have.

You will find that once you get into the habit of gratitude, you'll start to notice things to be grateful for, both small and large. Perhaps, somebody held a door for you, let your car through in traffic, or you got a promotion at work. When you start to look, you will find them.

Spend a couple of minutes on each gratitude. As you consider the experience, remember how it made you feel and enjoy replaying it over in your mind. Do this every day as you wake and just before falling asleep.

Reconnection Technique: Mindfully Reconnecting with Stillness

I wrote the following mindfulness technique for the book *Mindfulness for Transformation* (2020) by Shamash Alidina and the Teach Mindfulness Community. I call it 'Reconnecting with Stillness' and the audio is on the website:

Just taking a moment as you put your hands in the gassho, or prayer position, feel the pressure of skin contact, as your fingertips and promontories of your palms touch.

Be aware of the lightness of that touch, like the breath of an infant or the caress of a feather and very, very slowly begin to slide your hands up and down.

Gently begin to reconnect with the tips of your fingers, the hollow palm of your hand, and the fleshy part at the base of the thumb. Those parts of you that are unique to you, just like every snowflake is unique, our fingertips and palms tell the story of who we are. Slower than you even think you can, feeling the lines in the skin, the love line and the lifeline, the routes of who you are and who you can become.

Becoming aware of the energy building. Connecting two parts of you. And slowly you begin to pattern interrupt the busy mind, bi-lateral stimulation of the brain, and you can do this with your eyes closed, focusing entirely on the sense of touch, of temperature, of warmth, of energy passing between the two.

Or you can do this with your eyes open, exploring the lines, the contours on the skin and fingertips, discovering this unique landscape of you and every possibility that waits for you. Looking closer, noticing that the tips of your fingers may be darker than the rest. There may be places on the palm which are darker or there may not, all the subtle tones and shades of you.

Just notice noticing.

For additional resources, visit www.resiliencetemplate.com

Chapter 10

⁒

T is for (Self) Talk

'Self-love, my liege, is not so vile a sin, as self-neglecting.'

William Shakespeare

Many of us have a voice inside our head; sometimes it supports us, sometimes it disparages us. The negative voice that you hear inside your head that darkens your thoughts, is a problem for your mental fitness. Imagine if you were a top-class athlete and you became addicted to junk food. Consider the impact it would have on your physical fitness and your performance. The negative voice is the junk food that undermines your mental fitness. For many of us, the voice is not even ours. It belongs to a parent, or a teacher, or an ex-partner, or it could be an amalgam of people, but it never actually originated from us. Like a cuckoo in the nest, it has taken up residence in our minds.

Many people never even question it. They just accept that whatever critical thoughts they have are true. How many times have you called yourself an 'idiot' or 'stupid'? Is that really true? Or are you doing the best you can? As we move beyond old programming, old habitual thinking, towards a better relationship with ourselves, we start challenging that voice when it belittles and diminishes us. In short, we stand up to the bully.

For my bachelor's degree in education, I wrote my dissertation on bullying. A defining criterion for bullying is the imbalance of power because a bully is stronger in some way. That is often physically but it might be because bullies usually have allies. Not all of those in the bully's group join in the cruelty, but they are complicit and sway the balance of power by being part of it. School bullies may not be the only problem because bullies do not just appear on the playground. As children, critical parents and older adults are stronger than we are, and they can often develop into an internal bully voice. As adults, we might encounter bullies in our relationships or the workplace. Over our lifetime, multiple critical voices can fuse and become one voice. However it evolved, the bully voice within us originated from a disparity in power, but now we are no longer powerless.

At age eleven, I was bullied at high school. I remember it was a difficult time at home, and up until that point, school had always been a sanctuary for me. As often happens, it started with small things, comments made aloud, and ostracisation. Over time it affected not only my confidence but also my energy levels. Constant conflict is exhausting. That depletion of energy happens whether the bully is somebody in your external environment or if the criticism comes from your head; both drain our energy and wear us out. When my best friend defected to the bully group, I became even more of a target. As time went on, I realised that I could no longer be passive and hope that this would pass. I surprised myself one day when the bully confronted me, and instead of shrinking away, I suggested that we meet outside the school and settle *her* differences once and for all. Perhaps unsurprisingly, she did not show, but afterwards, her aggression towards me settled. Once she realised that she could no longer control my actions, she backed off. Action underpins resilience.

During the research for my dissertation, I discovered that when bullied over time, the victim often becomes a bully. That might be that the child of bully parents becomes a bully at school, finding weaker children to abuse. Or a child bullied over time carries the bully's voice in their head and uses it to taunt themselves. I see people who left school, or the environment where they were bullied, many years prior, and yet instead of leaving the bullying behind, they rehome the critical bullying voice in their own heads. It is as though they took up the job where the bully left off. Some people are still bullying themselves thirty, forty, fifty years after leaving school, and they never even recognise it. They continue to blame the school bully for so much that has gone wrong in their adult life. Yet, they have been their own bully for years. It is often difficult to escape the bully who is resident in our head until we take significant action, including addressing our self-talk.

When we focus on our self-talk, it is important to consider the quality of our thoughts because they have a big effect on our mental health. If you believe that your thoughts are innocuous, unfortunately you are wrong. If you believe that all your thoughts are real, that too is untrue. It is estimated that we have between 6,000 and 50,000 thoughts each day, most of them repetitive and many of them not factual. Think of a conveyor belt filled with random thoughts passing through your head in a loop. They keep going round and round. Our conscious mind does not notice them unless we pull them from the conveyor belt and choose to engage with them. Remember in Chapter 6, we said that our conscious mind can only be aware of between five and nine things at a time? The rest swim in our subconscious, like fish swim in water. Your mind is the water not the fish.

How you communicate internally, your self-talk. creates your reality of the world. Whether or not you realise it, you are the author of your own story. Have you ever wondered how thoughts work? Why do some have more influence over us than others? Why can two people have different opinions about the same thing? Here is the thought process very simply:

A stimulus occurs, it could be something that we see, hear, feel, smell or taste.

We interpret and make meaning of what has occurred by putting it through our filters of perception.

These filters include perceptions that are unique to us, based on our own experiences, circumstances, parental dogma, and beliefs about ourselves and the world.

Then there are the filters we all share to some extent. Those of generalisation; *Everything always goes wrong*, deletion; *Nothing good ever happens to me* and distortion; *This is the worst thing that ever happened.*

We have now interpreted the stimulus, made a personal

decision about what it means to us, and our interpretation creates emotions around what we believe happened.

Finally, these emotions determine our response and our behaviour, and we act accordingly.

As you can see, instead of being harmless, our thoughts are forceful and coercive. They are our personal lenses through which we interpret the world. Two people can experience the same event and come away with totally opposing views, and it all depends on their filters and perspective. Think back to the story, in Chapter 3, of two men in a restaurant. Both ate the same meal; one was in a good place and enjoyed his evening whilst the other was angry, and he used his meal as an excuse to vent. We all create our own models of reality, as shown in the thought process explanation above. If we create them, then we can recreate them in a more useful way and working with our thoughts is fundamental to making positive life changes.

Journal Exercise: Labelling thoughts

A truly effective way to improve your mental health is to become aware of your thoughts. Take time to stop and notice them. Question and challenge them. Stop accepting everything in your head at face value. As you challenge them, label them, and place them under three headings: *useful, non-useful,* and *not appropriate.* By *not appropriate,* I mean that the thought in and of itself might be fine, but I could be focusing on it at an inappropriate time. For example, during a job interview, I do not want to be thinking about what I will eat for dinner. Acknowledge the thoughts, label them, and put them aside to return to at another time. The aim is to notice but not engage with them. If the *non-useful* list is lengthy, it will give you a good idea of the quality of your thoughts and, therefore, your mental health.

Use your journal to record them. If you have ever had to balance finances or pay bills, you know how important it is to keep an eye on spending. This is similar. But in this case, we are monitoring how much time we spend on unhelpful thinking. Once you start to notice your thoughts, you will become more accountable for them. The alternative is to continue to operate on autopilot. The conveyor belt of your thoughts will keep looping around, affecting your emotions, behaviour, beliefs, and energy levels and *problems* will regularly come out of left field and knock you sideways.

Once you start double-checking the validity of what you are thinking, you will be surprised at how you can begin to change the soundtrack in your mind.

We often forget that thoughts are not facts; many are the products of our imagination. For example, I could think, *I am a purple alien, my two heads are exact opposites of each other, and my four legs are gangly.* Is this true? What makes this thought any less true than any negative thoughts I may have about my worth, looks, or life? When we hold it up to the light of day, it is clearly nonsense. Now we begin to hold our regular thoughts, especially those that are not useful, up to examination in the daylight and see them as they truly are.

Remember that by sustaining poor thoughts, 'stinking thinking', as the Alcoholics Anonymous (AA) twelve-step program calls it, then you are perpetuating their existence. Equally, by ignoring them, you are also prolonging their existence. Jung used the expression 'What you resist persists'.

Ignoring things does not make them go away; in fact, just the opposite happens. If you usually distract yourself so that you can ignore problems, instead try focusing on the issue, thought, or feeling. Give it full attention and notice how much better you feel. It is like when we have a task building up, in my case the ironing, which we keep putting off, but it feels great when you finally force yourself to tackle it. Treat your thoughts in the same way.

If we do not start to challenge our non-useful thoughts, they continue to grow, getting more and more destructive and increasingly embedded in our neural pathways. They become the voice of the self-saboteur holding us back and keeping us from the achievements that surely lie ahead. We can convince ourselves of anything if we repeat it often enough. Our mind does not differentiate between what is real and what we *think* is real. Knowing this, we can consciously think differently about ourselves and our life situation. We focus on the positive repeatedly; see it, feel it, hear it. That is the essence of how we fire and wire the neurons in our brain, embedding new neural pathways that become better beliefs and better behaviour patterns.

Thoughts affect our emotions, and our emotions affect our behaviour. Imagine a set of temporary traffic lights, set up and left for a few weeks, at one end of town. The impact of the lights is felt all over as traffic backs up. To avoid the jams, drivers increase traffic flow in other areas of town. Suddenly, instead of getting through town in a matter of minutes, short journeys are now longer, and the impact is widely felt. Tempers are frayed, and patience is low. This is how our bodies become when we get stuck in an emotion. When they get stuck, when we cannot let go of a problem, when we are constantly mulling over conversations that we have had or ruminating on things that somebody has *done* to us, we just do not move on, and often we get stuck on this negative road. If we stay stuck, if we cannot or will not snap out of *it*, then everything begins to back up. Our focus becomes tunnel visioned as we return to the issue repeatedly. It affects our sleep, we are constantly wearied by unhelpful thoughts and feelings, and it is exhausting. This is what we see on the surface; somebody who is preoccupied and often unable to see the bigger picture. Beneath the surface, we are producing adrenaline and cortisol, and long term, these will have a negative effect on our physical bodies.

When energy gets stuck, we begin to impact those around us. There are people who are energy vampires, they drain us with their negative outlook. Equally, there are others who are energy lifters, people who energise and make us feel better about ourselves. Your energy is not just yours, it impacts those around you. The question is, do you want to be an energy vampire or an energy lifter?

This chapter focuses on self-talk because it is so important. James was struggling with sleep because of the constant negative narrative running through his head. He had convinced himself that the world is a bad place with nothing to offer him. He talked about his love of disaster movies and the need he had to watch the news programmes several times each day. I suggested that whilst he was finding things difficult, he might ration the amount of news he watched, particularly switching off the television at 9 p.m., and pick another genre of films to watch. Instantly his face fell, and he said it would be impossible to change his viewing habits as television and films were the only way he found to relax.

Consider the thought, *it's going to be impossible, it's the only way I relax.* You must be careful what you say to yourself because you can convince yourself of anything if you repeat it often enough. Also, beware of falling into the trap of using double negatives, avoid using phrases like, *it's not going to be as bad as I first thought to give up television after 9 p.m.* because your brain will focus on the word *bad.* Instead, you give a positive counter to the thought, saying to yourself *it's going to be great to sleep better and have a calmer head.* When you focus on the positive and use only positive language you begin to bring some discipline to an anxious mind.

Self-Talk Technique: Pay It Forward

It might sound odd, but a way to support your own self-talk is to become more encouraging to others. How often has a thought crossed your mind that somebody looks nice? That you like their new hairstyle? Or that they did a lovely thing? We often might think it, but we do not always say it. Make a promise to start paying more compliments. When you do, notice if the other person happily accepts your compliment or seems embarrassed. If they look bashful, take this as a sign that they too may lack confidence; they may have a critical voice putting them down. The kinder you are to others, the kinder you will be to yourself. Try it – it is contagious.

As part of your daily routine, it is important to be kind to yourself, reminding yourself how well you are doing and how far you have come, acknowledging improvement as it happens. To reprogramme the mind and override poor habitual thinking keep reinforcing what it is doing right and accept that it will take time to feel natural to you.

Self-Talk Technique: Mirror Neurons

This is a useful exercise for you to change your self-talk. Set two minutes on a timer and look at yourself in a mirror. Gaze deeply into your eyes – remember how good it feels when somebody you love looks right into your eyes – and make positive affirmations about yourself.

Here are some suggestions of things you might say:

I am healthy

I am enough

I can do this

I am a good person

Repeat for at least two minutes, several times each day. If you break eye contact reset the two minutes and start again. Use this technique each time you clean your teeth or pass a mirror. You can build confidence in your appearance, your qualities, and your abilities. Remind yourself how great you are by using this technique daily. Remember, your mind does not differentiate between what is real and what you *think* is real. When you say *I am enough* your mind takes it as fact, when you repeat it over time, you genuinely come to believe it, and when you believe it you act on it and live it. Anything that you would like to change or accept can be created in this manner, effectively reprogramming your beliefs about yourself.

For additional resources, visit www.resiliencetemplate.com

Chapter 11

N is for Now

'Don't live in the past, don't ponder about the future, stay at the PRESENT moment NOW...always.'

Mark Twain

There are words in the dictionary that you might never come across because the vocabulary of language is so vast. Some of the words that you do encounter will sound strange to you because they are so unfamiliar. The word *now* is not one of these words. It is one of the top seventy-five most frequently used words in the English language. It means at present or in this moment. It is seemingly a word without ambiguity. It is simple. It is honest. It is immediate. It has authority, but sometimes we forget the power of now because it is a word we can confuse with phrases like 'in a minute' or 'later' or 'when I'm ready'.

Yet the word *now* gives present time context to the maps that we create. If we use our maps wisely, we make decisions that affect the only time in our life that we can profoundly influence and change–now. We can hope that we are lucky enough to be given extra time, but it is not a given. I lost my best friend when she was thirty-two and my partner when he was fifty-four; time is a gift that not all of us will have. It makes sense to value the life that you have now. If you value it, you will live well.

Now has two siblings, 'own' and 'won', and together, the three are an anthem for mental health because when we own the now, we have won.

In *Fahrenheit 451* (1953), Ray Bradbury said, 'It doesn't matter what you do…so long as you change something from the way it was before you touched it into something that's like you after you take your hands away.'

'It doesn't matter what you do' so long as you act and do something. The greatest threat to your mental fitness is being passive. Just like when you go to the gym, you participate, and you take action. Often at the start, it feels uncomfortable, but you push through the discomfort, overcoming obstacles because you are focused on a better plan.

Resilient people act. They do something every day that is good for their mental health. We know that it is easier to change a behaviour or action than to change thoughts or feelings. If you hide away when you feel low, then go out and face the world. If you stop going to the gym when you feel down, then go to the gym as you normally would. If you stay in bed and hide under the covers when you feel depressed, then get up and sit in the garden. Just do something different to break your habitual pattern. If you do nothing to change the status quo, then everything stays the same, and you remain trapped by the glass ceiling of your comfort zone.

Sometimes, I hear that 'I am not ready to change', and I am not always sure what it means. Just like the word happiness or the word love, readiness means different things to different people. It might mean when a person thinks they will have more time. It might mean when their business or career is going well. It might mean when they are better off financially. Or it might mean when their children have left home. Perhaps it means that they will feel ready when they feel less tired or sad. Feelings are part of the problem. They are old barometers by which we measure our current peace of mind. We can be ready even if we do not feel prepared because we know that feelings are based on old, outdated programming and patterns of behaviour. We know that feelings are not facts. There may be times when you may have done things when you did not feel like it and felt better for it. That is because you chose not to succumb to an old feeling that was based on old stories and old reactions. It was not relevant to this version of you, and it was not in your best interest. Feeling ready and being ready are hugely different things. If you are alive, you are ready to change.

It is not a surprise that we are often our own biggest saboteurs on the journey to transformation. A common story that we tell ourselves is that we do not have enough time. Yet when we break it down, there are 24 hours in a day and 7 days in a week. That totals 168 hours a week. Even allowing for time spent at work and time spent sleeping there is ample time for us to improve our life situation, our view of the world, and our long-term health.

In Chapter 12, we will look at scheduling opportunities to embed change incrementally throughout the day because repetition builds habits and so is non-negotiable. Just like eating, drinking, and sleeping, positive participation in our lives is essential.

Lots of us write 'to-do lists', things that we prioritise each day. To change your life, make implementing change a priority.

Be vigilant and notice the time vampires cropping up to distract and disturb you. Notice texts that sidetrack you, emails that belong in your junk files, or social media posts that divert you. If you have the facility on your mobile phone, keep track of how much time you spend on your phone, it is quite an eye-opener.

Consider the criteria that you use to measure how successful your day has been. Then decide to do more of that. Conversely, if your days seem unsuccessful, then shake them up and find better solutions.

Earlier, I mentioned eating, drinking, and sleeping because we all understand that these are vital to our survival. Mental resilience is too. The fact that it has been undervalued and misunderstood over the years does not diminish its importance for our health and well-being. We have a circadian rhythm that is necessary for good sleep. We have a digestive system that functions best at certain times of the day. Even though we may not always be able to adhere to the structure of these physical cycles–for example, if we do night work–it is important to do our best to work with them and not against them. Otherwise, we risk stacking up additional problems. The same is true of our mental health, we work with it not against it. Every day building resilience and personal strength and using the routine of our day as the rhythm which shapes change.

Sally talked of stress and her ballooning weight. Every evening after work, she went straight to an exercise class or to the gym and then ate her evening meal at 9.30 p.m., and she was disappointed because, despite her efforts, her weight remained the same. I explained that the body is not designed to eat so late and that working out when you are stressed adds more stress to the bucket. Stress and the fight or flight response affect our digestive system. Unbeknown to her, she was compromising her digestive system in several ways, and her body never had time to recalibrate and rest properly. I suggested that we work *with* her body rather than against it. I asked if she would consider eating earlier, cutting down her exercise regime for a while, and using techniques to reduce stress? She thought about it and said no. Instead, she asked me to install a gastric band under hypnosis. I explained that I could not do that because I believed that it would simply bypass the problem, and so she decided to find another hypnotherapist who would do the gastric band for her. I respected her choice. When looking to change, we do have to be careful because our desire for a quick fix and our old mindset can be a big part of the problem, a self-help saboteur.

This brings me to the most significant question in this chapter 'What will you do now to improve your mental fitness?'

Now Technique: Keep A Journal Every Day

Until this point, you have used a journal at intervals to help with your planning and to assess the quality of your mental health. Now I would like you to use your journal every day.

Consider that the hairdresser keeps a record of the tints used, the bank teller of deposits and withdrawals. Supermarkets record what sells and what does not. Record keeping is essential. A journal is useful in several ways:

It acts an aide-mémoire

It is an opportunity to offload

It keeps us accountable

It charts our journey

It records our successes.

Done properly, it can be a catalyst for a change, an opportunity for self-reflection, and a store-cupboard of the best pick me ups. Poorly done, it can be a list of recrimination and misery. It does not have to be a simple paper record; you can add drawings and pictures, pressed flowers, and any items that inspire and motivate.

Find time each day to record what worked for you, notice your feelings and emotions, and keep a tally of the techniques you used and when. Remember that some techniques may work at different times, so you can move things around to fit your routine better. Once a week, take time to look back through your journal, highlight successes, and plan the week ahead accordingly. Use it as a document for change and a log of progress. Remember to double-check that you are being consistent with the techniques, not just using those you find less challenging. You can expect some element of discomfort initially, just like when you first exercise at the gym. Stepping out of your comfort zone is not only essential but also fundamental to your success.

Now Technique: WINS

Alongside your journal, many of you will run a daily diary. Like a journal, it helps us plan our day and sets out the tasks we need to complete. Diaries keep us on track, especially at work, because they focus us. Have you ever double-booked an appointment or failed to write a commitment down in your diary? Chaos often ensues. I like to prioritise my tasks in my diary by using the following acronym, WIN, which means Willingness to Initiate Now.

At the start of the day, choose three things that you are willing to initiate now. Let these be the first things that you clear from your to-do list each day. At the end of the week, anything still left on your to-do list should become the WINs on Monday morning. If you find that you are struggling to complete certain tasks, you may want to consider what is holding you back from clearing them; this itself might be another issue.

Many of the techniques that I have included serve another purpose, and that is to pattern interrupt. If you notice that you revert to certain patterns of behaviour or ways of thinking during difficult times, then pattern interrupting and putting in conscious changes will move you forward. For example, if normally when feeling depressed you ignore the telephone, then by answering it you break your old pattern. Once you notice you are stuck, apply a technique to distract from older, less useful behaviour.

Living in the now means not regretting the past or ruminating about the future. Many of us deplete our energy going over things that can no longer be changed or problems that might never happen. Mark Twain said,

'I've lived through some terrible things in my life, some of which actually happened.'

Statistically, about 98 per cent of the things that we worry about never actually happen.

Learning how to be mindful, accepting thoughts as neither fact nor fiction but simply as random samples that pop into our mind is an excellent place to begin living in the present.

Now Technique: Mindfully Detaching from Thoughts

Set sixty seconds on a timer, and as you do so, close your eyes and focus on the breath.

Notice the air as it flows into your mouth or nose and notice the temperature of that air as it enters and leaves your body.

Notice whether you find this easy to follow or whether you struggle to track the flow of the breath.

Know that there is no right or wrong here; we are merely setting aside sixty seconds to stop and reconnect with the breath.

If thoughts come to mind, as they will, accept that a thought is just a thought and let it go.

Each time, come back to the breath, breathing in, and breathing out.

Notice how that felt. Was it difficult to keep focused? Were you distracted by thoughts or by your environment? It is worth practising this exercise three times a day. As you improve, extend the time until you can spend at least five minutes mindfully noticing your thoughts. There is an audio version on the website.

For additional resources, visit www.resiliencetemplate.com

Chapter 12

⤤

E is for Embed Change

'The eight laws of learning are explanation, demonstration, imitation, repetition, repetition, repetition, repetition, repetition.'

John Wooden

Imagine if, as children, along with dental hygiene, we were taught good *mental hygiene*. I wonder how different things would be if we were encouraged to follow a good daily mental fitness routine. How would it be if it was customary to have regular mental health check-ups and if there was no stigma to having remedial work? The Resilience Template™ is a blueprint for good *mental hygiene*. I hope that in time maintaining mental health will become as natural to us as daily dental care.

This chapter covers how we develop good *mental hygiene* and build new habits to increase our mental fitness. It also offers suggestions and easy ways to embed The Resilience Template™ techniques into a daily routine.

Statistics vary on how long it takes to form new habits. That is because much depends on what we are trying to change. One popular method is the 21/90 rule, which works as follows: firstly, commit to a new habit for 21 days, after which time it will feel more natural to you. Secondly, continue the new habit for another 90 days; during this time you will embed it.

Following the 21/90 rule, I suggest that you practise each of the techniques for 21 days to develop familiarity and then continue them for a further 90 days. Start with the exercises in Chapter 7: P is for Preparation. If, after 21 days, you do not feel noticeably calmer, then do the exercises in this chapter for longer. It is better to calm the nervous system before adding further exercises from the subsequent chapters.

How We Learn

The way we learn is influenced by genetics, consistency, application, and the relevance we give to our learning. Visit any early years class, and you will see children passing milestones at different times. Whether it is tying shoelaces, getting dressed for sport, or learning to read and write, children will develop skills in their own time. Any parent knows that no matter their drive and perhaps their frustration, their child will learn at their own pace. What we do know, however, is that repetition and consistency are the fundamental keys to learning.

The Resilience Template™ is predicated on using simple

techniques repeated at regular intervals throughout the day. It is the repetition that will lead to successful change. The more often you use the techniques, the sooner you will see improvements in your mental health. Remember that one of the pillars of resilience is planning and, in this chapter, we plan how we will schedule the exercises each day.

We learn better when we see the value of things, and therefore, it is incredibly important when acquiring a new skill to make it relevant. If I have somebody who is always prepared to dress me, a parent, for example, why would I feel any need to learn how to dress? However, once something becomes relevant, and I am in a situation where I need to take responsibility for it, then I am likely to have more incentive to learn the skill. Take the child in school again, peer pressure and the desire to conform will provide a new impetus for learning how to dress himself.

I used to teach modern foreign languages; a vital component of lesson planning was making the subject relevant to the students. If we do not see the relevance of something, we are more likely to discard it. This is a good place to pause to consider why improving mental fitness is currently relevant to you.

Journal Exercise: Relevance, Why Mental Fitness Is Important to Me

Take some time to consider why mental fitness is relevant for you. Reflect on what it means to you. Use your journal to record your thoughts. As things occur to you, come back to the exercise. The greater depth you can apply to this task, the more conviction you will have in applying the changes and persevering when challenges occur.

Challenges can be external and internal. As much as possible, remove any external focuses like timescales and goals; they are distractions. Instead, focus internally because that is where change begins. We are all unique and we progress at different rates; if I set myself the target that I will have improved my mental fitness in four weeks, and it does not happen that quickly, I am likely to feel disheartened. Despite any progress made so far, any perceived failure might lead to discouragement, with the result that I might choose to quit altogether. That is why it is best to avoid timescales.

Along with time scales, many of us also set ourselves specific goals. I avoid these too because changing mindset is complex. When we transform our mindset, we replace habits and beliefs that we hold at our core and slowly transform the narrative underpinning our current life. Change, both good and bad, occurs over time, and by accepting that we are all a work in progress, we can recognise the futility of setting a *completion* date in our diaries. Goal setting focuses too much on getting what we perceive is the *right* result. Sometimes, the result that we want turns out not to be right for us. So, if we set intentions rather than goals, we permit ourselves some flexibility. This ability to be flexible is important because it supports us even if our priorities change. It avoids overwhelm, which we can unwittingly cause ourselves, due to the size of the task at hand. We know that when something appears too daunting, we are more likely to give up.

It is much better to set intentions rather than be governed by timescales and goals. For example, 'My intention today is to do my exercises as planned.' Live in the now. If something important gets in the way today, then reset your intention tomorrow. Set intentions just for today and use them to shape each day. I am a Reiki practitioner trained in the Usui School of Reiki, and I find the Reiki intentions incredibly useful:

Just for today, do not worry

Just for today, do not anger

Just for today, earn your living honestly

Just for today, show gratitude to every living creature

Just for today, honour your parents, teachers, and elders.

These are such gentle intentions to live by and immensely powerful. If things do not work out as planned today, then I set the intention to begin again tomorrow. In this way, I avoid the judgement which comes with *lack* (in this case, lack of achieving a goal) because I chose not to set a goal in the first place. Rather than be under the control of an external target I maintain control by setting personal intentions and using these to map each day.

Other factors impact the speed and the depth at which we change including context, self-awareness, and support from the people who mean most to us.

Context matters because we cannot separate our attempts to change from our life situation. We have jobs, relationships, and many challenges to manage. We juggle our responsibilities every day, and we must fit in our mental fitness work around other priorities. Later in the chapter, I describe how to do this.

Self-awareness is fundamental to change. Without it, we go through life on autopilot, caught up in old habitual thoughts and behaviour, and not recognising how generally decent we are. When we develop self-awareness, we choose to live in the present to free ourselves from thoughts of past or future, and in doing so, we become more mindful. Along with mindfulness, the STOPP protocol we use in the next chapter is a good technique to increase self-awareness. It trains us to step back, observe our emotions, and become proactive rather than reactive.

A great aid to improving our mental health is to enlist the support of family and friends. When we are close to something, it can be hard to monitor objectively. Change can be like a dripping shower; when you first notice it, the noise can drive you to distraction, but often there comes the point when the shower stops dripping all by itself, and you never even noticed it stop. Initially, like the sound of the shower, the changes that we implement can grate and leave us feeling uncomfortable. They are so different from anything we have ever done before that, at times, the voice of resistance deafens us, and we might consider giving up. This is normal, stepping out of our comfort zone can be difficult but that is no reason to stop. Using the techniques diligently will bring about fundamental and steady change. This is why it can be useful to tell family and friends what you are doing because they often notice the difference before you do.

Embedding New Habits

Later in this chapter we will consider how to incorporate the techniques into your daily practice. Once we have come up with a plan and you feel more comfortable using the techniques, we can ensure that the techniques themselves do not add another layer of pressure to your schedule, or more stress to your life.

The Resilience Template™ is designed so that the techniques slot into your daily routine, and we do this by hooking them on to existing habits. We already have a set of habits operated by the subconscious mind, for example, teeth brushing, washing up, walking, boiling the kettle. These provide the perfect structure on which we can hang the techniques. The exercises become automatically easier to manage, reducing pressure on ourselves because we are already doing these tasks every day, and by slotting the exercises into our existing routine, we are more likely to do them. The Resilience Template™ is so successful because it provides context, structure, and a schedule.

Our subconscious mind regulates so many essential functions, including breathing, heart rate, and the digestive system. It also controls many of our daily tasks, which over time have become regular habits, like how we get dressed or wash the dishes. We do so many things directly from our subconscious mind that we barely concentrate on them; they are familiar to us. The aim of The Resilience Template™ is that these techniques will similarly become embedded patterns of behaviour. If you stop to consider your teeth brushing method, the process might look something like this:

1. Pick up the toothpaste
2. Take off the lid
3. Pick up your toothbrush
4. Put toothpaste on your brush
5. Turn on the tap
6. Put the brush under the tap
7. Turn off the tap
8. Raise your toothbrush to your mouth
9. Brush your teeth in your familiar sequence
10. Remove the brush

11. Spit out toothpaste
12. Turn on the tap
13. Rinse the brush
14. Rinse the sink
15. Turn off the tap
16. Put the lid on the toothpaste
17. Put toothbrush and toothpaste away.

There are a lot of steps to do a simple task. Imagine how long it would take us to do all our daily mundane chores if we had to consider each action. Luckily, the subconscious mind takes the tasks on, does them habitually, and is both supervisor and operator. Once the subconscious mind has ingrained a habit, it can be difficult to change it. This is why changes to our routine can be unsettling because they cause us to act against the subconscious mind itself.

Think about how you drive your car. Once you are proficient as a driver, you do not consciously put your foot on the clutch, change the gears, and so on; your trained mind does the task automatically. But do you remember how it felt to be a learner driver? At times, you probably wondered if you would ever learn to drive confidently. You did, of course, but it took time to etch the task in the neural pathways of your mind. We are doing the same with The Resilience Template™ techniques.

Liz came to see me because she had difficulty driving at night. She struggled because she could not see her feet or the pedals in the dark. The problem was that Liz was still operating from her conscious mind and consciously following the driving script: depress the clutch, change gear, release the clutch, and so on. It was not natural for her to operate the pedals with her feet, and so she kept looking down, firstly to locate them and secondly to apply the correct foot. In daylight, although not entirely practical, she could see the pedals if she looked down, and so she could drive adequately, but at night this was not possible. She had not yet trained her mind sufficiently in the task of driving; it had not become a natural habit for her, and so it was not yet embedded in her subconscious mind. Resolution came when she focused on driving in daylight only, enabling her conscious mind to absorb the process by automatically learning the correct foot position. Once her conscious mind grasped the skill, the subconscious mind could take over, and she no longer needed to check her feet and pedals.

It feels awkward learning new skills. It is natural to think that this is due to the level of difficulty, but it is because there are no existing neural pathways in the brain which have encoded the memory of how to do these new things. That is why repetition is so important, it forges new pathways in the brain, and these pathways embed the memory of the activity. Then once a task is learnt, it becomes encoded and the subconscious mind takes over the operation from our conscious mind.

The techniques in The Resilience Template™ may be unfamiliar now, but with repetition you will learn to do them well. There will come a point when they feel natural, and the result will be a set of new habits supporting your mental fitness. Then your mindset will improve exponentially. This is the control that many of us crave. Creating the mindset that we choose rather than the one we inherited over the years.

The exercises are easy to learn; they require repetition to embed them but do not equate simplicity to their level of usefulness. The Brazilian novelist Paulo Coelho said, 'It's the simplest things in life that are the most extraordinary; only wise men are able to understand them.'

Journal Exercise: List Your Daily Habits

Look at the habits and routines that you already have. In your journal, make a list of the things that you do consistently and repeatedly throughout your day. Here are some suggestions:

1. Wake up
2. Clean my teeth
3. Wash my hands
4. Wait for a kettle to boil
5. Work at the computer
6. Wash dishes
7. Walk to my car or outside with the dogs
8. Sit in traffic
9. Put on and remove my makeup
10. Go to bed.

The next step is to link the techniques we have learnt in the 7 steps to your existing habits. It is entirely personal at which points in your day you practise the exercises, but many will slot naturally into small gaps in your day.

Here are some suggestions:

1. As you wake each day, spend a few minutes practising the Reconnection Technique for gratitude, from Chapter 9. When we visualise and create feelings about those things, or people, for whom we are grateful we build on the positive associations in our life.

2. Straight after teeth cleaning, spend two minutes doing the Mirror Neurons (Self) Talk Technique. Remind yourself that you are resilient, valued, and capable.

3. After hand washing, stand in front of a mirror and spend two minutes practising the Preparation Technique: 3-2-1 Reset, to recalibrate the nervous system and leave you feeling grounded.

4. Whilst waiting for the kettle to boil, practise the Acceptance Technique: The Soothing Tap to manage stress and leave you feeling grounded.

5. When working at the computer, set a timer every 25 minutes. Spend a few minutes practising some of the preparation exercises like the 4-2-7 Breathing technique, Square Breathing, or the 3-2-1 Reset technique.

6. Try doing a daily task mindfully. When washing the dishes take an extra minute to notice and enjoy the moment, experiencing the heat from the water, the softness of the bubbles, the texture of the skin as it begins to wrinkle, and so on. Simply take time out from the rush to notice and be present.

7. Walking to the car or with the dog, practise the Reconnection Technique: Five, Four, Three, Two, One in Chapter 9.

8. In a parked car or at your desk, take sixty seconds to mindfully detach from your thoughts as we did in Chapter 11. It takes a minute to practise stepping back.

9. At any time during the day, take a few minutes to

listen to the Progressive Muscle Relaxation; the bonus track is available on the website. Stopping for a few minutes, throughout the day, will increase your awareness and prevent stress and anxiety build-up.

10. At bedtime, spend a few minutes practising the Reflection Technique: The Cinema, in the next chapter. Reflect on your day, cherry pick the positive experiences and express gratitude for being tucked safely up in bed. When we are grateful we sleep better.

Use time spent on hold on the phone or moments in the bath to practise. When you have a morning cup of tea, slot in a technique. After lunch, try a short relaxation exercise, or listen to a recording after your evening meal. By now, you have the picture – think outside the box. Think small, think incremental. Be creative. This is how you transform your life.

When you have practised a technique or drawn on one in a real situation, take time to praise this improvement in your behaviour. Encouragement keeps us all going in the right direction so remember to give acknowledgement where it is due. This can be hard initially, for many of us it can take some time to feel comfortable using self-praise. That is normal so use your journal to record your successes and to act as a reminder to credit yourself. Every time you challenge poor thinking or find the time to relax or accept things you cannot change, applaud yourself for prioritising your mental health. Each time you stop to appreciate a moment, consciously let a worry go, or remind yourself that you are worth it, you build another layer of resilience.

Creating a healthy mindset is easy; all we need to do is treat ourselves as though we were talking to the person we love most in the world.

Above all, remember that beginnings are delicate times; be kind to yourself.

For a suggested daily timetable and additional resources, visit www.resiliencetemplate

Chapter 13

❦

R is for Reflection

'Life can only be understood backwards; but it must be lived forwards.'

Søren Kierkegaard

A pilot constantly readjusts the direction he flies to keep the plane on course. Like the pilot, we can get knocked off trajectory in our life plans, but that does not mean that we cannot continue to move forward. How differently would we approach life's problems if we had been prepared to expect strong winds and turbulence when we took the controls? Imagine if the challenges we face in life were all part of the plan. The truth is that even if we never realise it, many of us have always kept flying despite the difficult conditions.

In this chapter, we look at the seventh and final Resilience Template™ step: Reflection. Think of this step as a necessary pause, to stop and assess progress, and to replot the course if necessary. Reflection requires a peaceful mind and deep thought. Rather than actively participate in the overwhelm, we become observers. We need hindsight without judgement because judgement has an emotional element, and to be a detached observer we must let go of any emotional bias.

Reflection is not rumination or worry; it is exactly the opposite. If you want to see your reflection in a pool of water, then the water must be still. If there is any agitation, even the slightest ripple, then the reflection is distorted. Clarity lies within the calm.

Journal Exercise: The Weekly Check-in

Every seven days dedicate time to reflecting on your week. Consider what has and has not seemed a success to you. What are the defining differences that you notice?

As you incorporate The Resilience Template™ into your schedule, reflect too on which exercises gelled with you and which did not. If you have persevered with them for twenty-one days, but something is jarring with you, consider why. These are simple exercises but the meaning our minds give them may make some of us feel uncomfortable.

Change can be unsettling for human beings but possessing the ability to be flexible and to adapt is essential. We live in a world that is changing at a phenomenal rate. Whatever happens we must be resilient enough to cope.

Reflection Technique: The Cinema

First, sit quietly and focus on the rise and the fall of the breath. Breathing in. Breathing out.

If your mind should wander and get hooked by thoughts, that is okay. Bring it back to the breath when you notice. Breathing in. Breathing out.

Imagine you are at the cinema, sitting before a wide screen and, playing for you alone, is a replay of a painful event in your life. Notice this extension of you on the screen. This requires no involvement on your part, you are simply a detached observer. Simply watch. Breathing in. Breathing out.

Without getting drawn in by critical thinking and judgement, see the experience as it happened. Sit with the images as you remain withdrawn from the action.

Resist any emotional pull to get caught up in censure and blame. The aim of reflection is to seek feedback. Breathing in. Breathing out.

As you sit in stillness, consider this version of you with kindness and compassion. What do you know now that you did not know before? This is a rich seam of gold in your experience. Consider it deeply.

When you are ready, come back into the room with a smile and gratitude for the awareness you now have.

You can also use this technique to reflect on your experience of your resilience journey so far. The answers are there, you just have to be open to them. There is an audio version on the website.

Journal Exercise: Log Your Insights

Following the Cinema reflection technique use your journal to log your insights. Let the words flow; you can come back to them later. Once you have recorded these perceptions on paper, pause and take a few deep breaths. Now return to the page and underline the main points amongst the chatter. Armed with these observations, you can now toast your achievements and just like the pilot you can begin replotting your course where necessary.

Changing your mindset and mental fitness stirs up both the unfamiliar and the uncomfortable, accept that this is necessary. Accept too that you have the resilience to deal with whatever comes up for you. Your old patterns of behaviour have not always worked for you. Now it is time to embrace change. Einstein said it best, 'The definition of insanity is doing the same thing over and over again and expecting a different result.'

For fundamental change to happen, we need to shake the snow globe – this is our world as we currently experience it – and turn everything on its head. As the snow in the globe resettles, you will find that each snowflake has shifted slightly; change does this too in our lives. It does not always arrive in a blaze of glory but is usually, subtle and incremental. Slowly, over time, it moves us beyond the restrictions of our comfort zone to a landscape that is both familiar and transformative.

Reflection is a great opportunity for us to evaluate experiences, develop understanding and gain acceptance, all of which increase wisdom. Neuro-Linguistic Programming (NLP) teaches us to understand the language of the mind. In particular, the language of the subconscious mind. It is an excellent approach to use if you are interested in understanding more about how the mind works. One of the main presuppositions in NLP is 'There is no failure, only feedback.' This is truly liberating and reframes every experience we have ever had or will have. Taking time out for reflection gives us an opportunity to garner feedback and then to use that knowledge moving forwards. Nothing is wasted if we learn from it, and that includes past experiences and pain. It also means that we can build on our successes too, using them as a further frame for feedback. Take what works for you and build on it.

I did not always understand, but over time I have realised that everything that has happened in my life has brought me to the place where I am today. Not only that, but my former pain and experiences are a resource. I am fortunate because I lived in the shadowlands of the victim for many years, wanting better things but not knowing how to move forward. Reflection helped me to remove the excessive emotion around self-judgement, the pain from my upbringing, and the mistakes I have made as an adult. Reflection brought stillness, which helped me to accept my past experiences with compassion and find a purpose for it all. The Resilience Template™ is one purpose which motivates me because it gives me the chance to help others to work through their pain and become the scriptwriters of their own lives.

Reflection as a tool helps us rewrite the maps we have created. Just like the pilot we can recalibrate the direction and ensure that they remain relevant to our current lives. It also provides context; this is often the last piece of the jigsaw and seldom appears until after the event or until we take the time to calmly consider what happened. There is an ancient parable called *Blind Men and an Elephant*, that has been found in Buddhist, Hindu and Jain texts. It first dates from around 500 BCE and it provides an illustration of the importance of context. Below I have included a version from:

https://en.wikipedia.org/wiki/blind_men_and_an_elephant

A group of blind men heard that a strange animal, called an elephant, had been brought to the town, but none of them were aware of its shape and form. Out of curiosity, they said: 'We must inspect and know it by touch, of which we are capable'. So, they sought it out, and when they found it they groped about it. The first person, whose hand landed on the trunk, said, 'This being is like a thick snake'. For another one whose hand reached its ear, it seemed like a kind of fan. As for another person, whose hand was upon its leg, said, the elephant is a pillar like a tree-trunk. The blind man who placed his hand upon its side said the elephant, 'is a wall'. Another who felt its tail, described it as a rope. The last felt its tusk, stating the elephant is that which is hard, smooth and like a spear.

It is such a valuable story, reminding us that whilst our subjective experiences may be real, they also limit our ability to see the bigger picture or to accept that there are other truths beyond our own. Each man experienced something different, and each of them was right; what was missing was context. Sometimes, we get caught up thinking that there is only one truth but, just as in the elephant story, that is because we do not always see the full picture.

It can be hard to look back at an experience, especially if it caused pain. The temptation to simply move on, to brush things under the carpet and to try to forget them is strong. If we deliberately avoid opportunities for reflection, we lose valuable opportunities to learn about ourselves and our capabilities. We also deny ourselves a chance to gain feedback about how we cope with challenges. Many of us are stronger than we think, and we just do not give ourselves opportunities to realise it.

Linda came to see me one morning. On the way she had pulled out at a junction and almost caused an accident. When she arrived, she was angry with herself for what she called a stupid mistake. She did not want to talk about what had happened. She was preoccupied during the session and started getting angrier, slipping derogatory comments about herself into the conversation and becoming more emotional. I noticed that her story was changing too; blame for the other drivers was growing. As she rose to leave, I suggested that she stay a little longer and discuss the incident. Her initial response was, 'What for? What would it change?' She had decided that it was over and done with.

It is true that nothing we might say could change the facts of the incident, but I wondered if we could find some benefit, for Linda, from what had occurred. If we brush things away and carry on as though nothing happened, we often magnify the event itself, it becomes another monster under the bed, and we can develop strong emotions around the memories. When we link emotions to thoughts and events, we are more likely to create bigger problems in the long term. If by calmly discussing the facts we can minimise our emotional response we are more likely to process the incident. Excessive emotions are the glue that makes troublesome thoughts stick around. It is always better to dilute the emotional response if possible.

We practised some of the exercises to calm the nervous system: 4-2-7 Breathing and the 3-2-1 Reset exercise from Chapter 7. Once calmer Linda was able to reflect on what had happened. She was quiet for a while and then she said, 'It was my mistake, nobody else's.' She said that she had been rushing because she had overslept as she was sleeping badly. Sitting quietly, she realised that she had not slept properly for over a month because of rumours at work about redundancy. The chance to pause gave her time to consider and to answer the question 'What do you know now that you did not know before?'

She saw that she had not been handling the uncertainty at work as well as she had thought. Once she recognised this we considered what she could do to better manage the situation. She decided to be more proactive and speak honestly to her boss about her job security worries. This was a good outcome because action is one of the four pillars of resilience.

We all benefit when we stop and reflect because often we think we are dealing with one problem, in Linda's case the near collision, but in reality, we are dealing with something entirely different. Using the reflection techniques in The Resilience Template™ we can examine what is truly happening beneath the surface, and in doing so we can discover what is really disturbing our peace of mind.

Sam has Irritable Bowel Syndrome (IBS) and following advice from his doctor, he asked to learn some relaxation techniques to help him manage the symptoms. The symptoms of IBS do respond well to mindfulness and relaxation but there can be other factors. We chatted about his daily routine. He admitted that he is a late riser, usually getting up at the last possible moment and then rushing to work. On the drive to the office, he ate a cereal bar for breakfast, and he usually arrived late at work which was causing conflict with his boss who was increasingly frustrated by his employee's timekeeping and, by his unkempt appearance.

As he talked he fell into the trap of judgement as he criticised himself for being lazy and unmotivated. He was angry at himself for upsetting his boss and risking his job. Many of us use self-blame and recrimination, but it is not usually greatly productive.

Every morning, pressing the snooze button, he remonstrated with himself, and every morning he continued to press snooze. Remember the definition of insanity? Doing the same thing and expecting a different response.

He set his self-judgement aside to focus on the genuine problem of his IBS symptoms. He realised that he could address his timekeeping by getting up a little earlier. He would have time to eat a healthy breakfast, and then he could shower before setting off to work. Despite realising this he was not sure that he wanted to get up earlier, no matter the benefits. When he considered why, he had a surprise. He remembered that as a child, on very cold days, his mum had indulged him, letting him stay longer in bed and his subconscious mind had linked staying in a warm bed to fond memories of his mum. Once we find the emotional glue holding old beliefs in place, it is easier to change perspective.

I shared with him the five-step STOPP protocol which is a technique used in dialectical therapy, to develop distress tolerance. It is also an observation tool which is especially useful in reflection because it provides a structure for deeper thinking. Below I include the process which my client and I used. I have provided a simpler version of the protocol at the end of the chapter.

Stop We intend to make proactive rather than reactive decisions, and for that to happen, we need to stop and pattern interrupt old destructive ways of thinking, and behaviours. This break allows us to put some space between us and the immediate problem.

Take three deep belly breaths and put some distance between you and your thoughts by focusing solely on the breath. Breathing in. Breathing out.

His first thought was, 'I can't get up that early it will be awful.' Was this the voice of an adult looking to improve a difficult and painful health condition, or was it an outdated response related to a childhood morning habit?

Observe what are the thoughts and your reactions to them that are surfacing right now? Observe the emotions that arise and notice what you feel and where you feel it.

He experienced an overreaction to the suggestion that he get up a little earlier because of the emotional links his mind had attributed to his mother. His limiting thoughts justified old habits in a matter of milliseconds.

Perspective Can you pull back and sit with the response that you observed and challenge it? How would you advise a friend in a similar situation?

Consider the current facts of his life. Are the old habits based on his present life or on childhood when he did not have IBS? Consider the rewards of a stress-free start to the day, and do those benefits compensate for an earlier start? When we stop and review the facts, we no longer get swept up by out-dated responses. His health would improve if he began the day from a place of rest and digest rather than from the fight or flight stress position.

Practise what works and mindfully proceed. Use the STOPP technique frequently to analyse your default responses. The aim is to reverse less useful programming and to spot triggers. When we are mindful we are more likely to plan ahead in a way that is compatible with our current values.

We practise and embed healthier habits for the person we are today, not the child we were yesterday. When you are looking for the triggers you are seeking patterns that have built up. You become a forensic scientist, identifying habits and behaviours in your life which create stress.

By establishing a practical, calmer morning routine, Sam no longer engages the stress response first thing. This is important because we know that during fight or flight, the digestive system shuts down. Once we calm the nervous system, the digestion process will work more efficiently. Rising thirty minutes earlier will allow Sam to accomplish what he needs to do before work and this will ensure that his stress response remains muted. Reduced stress will positively impact his IBS symptoms.

When we develop the ability to recognise triggers we become less reactive. Now we are fire marshals rather than firefighters, no longer overreacting to random sparks. Instead we pause, breathe, observe and consider perspective; we are proactive not reactive.

Here is a simplified version of the STOPP protocol to adapt.

Reflection Technique: STOPP Protocol

Step 1: Stop and pause.

Step 2: Take three deep belly breaths and retreat from any emotional charge.

Step 3: Observe your emotions, feelings; what conclusions have you started to come to (rightly or wrongly)?

Step 4: Perspective. Which filters of perception are you basing these feelings and conclusions on? Is this response valid and congruent with the version of you right now? Have you considered context?

Step 5: Practice. To change your mindset, mindfully practise this technique every day

Daily repetition will embed it as you learn to sharpen your skills. Start small. Reflect on your day, reflect on its challenges, and reflect on your mood. Also, reflect on The Resilience Template™ exercises. Which exercise challenges you the most? Which calms you? Which makes you think of quitting altogether? Which do you look forward to?

When you are confident with the technique, use it to reflect on some of your experiences from the past, always asking yourself, 'What do I now know – about myself and the situation – that I didn't know before?' Is it that you are stronger than you think? That despite challenges, nothing lasts forever, including difficulty? Is it that you are resilient, that you are flexible, pragmatic, a planner, and a person of action?

If necessary, use the insights you gain to change course as you continue to transform your life. As with so many other elements in The Resilience Template™, reflection is a skill. You have lots of time to learn how to do it well.

For additional resources, visit www.resiliencetemplate.com

Chapter 14

ℰℱℴ

Moving Forward

'I will drink life to the lees.'

Alfred Lord Tennyson

If you have reached this chapter, having worked through the book and followed each step, by now you will have seen changes in your mental health. You will have spent several weeks doing The Resilience Template™ preparation exercises, and you will be feeling calmer. Finding that you have much more clarity and confidence in your capacity for change, you have begun to change your approach to living.

You have given up fighting the disappointments and frustrations, and in doing so, you have started to let go of your pain and accept 'what is'.

You are now learning to value yourself and have created a reconnection built on self-love and compassion.

You regularly challenge the critical self-talk, the inner voice, and the commentary inside your head. Your focus is now on the cheerleader within you who encourages and supports you every day.

You have accepted the considerable power of acting 'now'. Understanding that no matter the time we spend worrying about the past or projecting worries about the future, the only time we can make a difference is now.

You have built up hours of transformation time, which has slotted into your daily routine and the exercises have become more natural to you.

You now spend the time you deserve on reflection, reminding yourself how incredible you are and how strong you have always been. Max Ehrmann's advice in the Desiderata resonates,

'Beyond a wholesome discipline, be gentle with yourself. You are a child of the universe no less than the trees and the stars, you have a right to be here.'

You should feel incredible because it is all true. Without you, the universe would not be the same. You are a vital part of the whole. You matter. We all do. Now is the time to live the life you choose, foregoing any other plan for you.

Imagine that you have heard your story for the first time and feel compassion. You are unique; there is no other version of you. Never compare yourself to others; there are no comparisons to make. Never take for granted how far you have come and, more importantly, how far you will go.

You have begun to plan but remember that the plan will change as you change. Things that once seemed important will feel less so. Your priorities will shift as you transform.

I remember as a little girl when I first got glasses. Suddenly the world was different. My plan in the classroom was always to copy the blackboard notes from my friend's book; now I no longer needed that plan. I could read the board for myself. The change felt like a miracle. A simple alteration to the lens, the filter through which I saw the world, and suddenly there was definition. Everything had a shape, things were no longer blurred, and colours were suddenly vibrant. I had been struggling with blurry vision for so long that I had forgotten what the world looked like. I remember marvelling at everything I saw, as though it was the first time I had ever seen it. At first, I hated wearing my glasses; they felt uncomfortable and strange. I did not look like 'me' in them. There was some name-calling from some of the children, and part of me wanted to return to the safety of how I was before. I had no choice but to persist and, despite the challenges, I loved experiencing this new world. It was bright and bold and breathtaking. The Resilience Template™ approach offers a new lens through which to view the world, it is a new pair of glasses. This world is wonderful, at times scary, and always challenging. Wear your new glasses with pride and persevere. It is worth it.

Our whole world recalibrates when we accept our good fortune and focus on what we have. We see things as they are. We have a physical body. Maintenance is our responsibility. We have mental fitness. Mental hygiene is our responsibility. We have opportunities. Identifying and acting on them is our responsibility. There is a palace of possibilities waiting for us once we let go of our fear and explore them. Remember, always to practise gratitude; it is the key to the palace. In each part of our lives there are moments for which we can be grateful.

We are each a gift to the world. unique stars in the universal firmament. Now we can make a commitment to manage stress, to change for our own sake and the sake of those around us. It is not always easy, but the best things in life never are. There will be times when you slip up. That is fine. This is a book about resilience, not about perfection. Each slip up will be feedback, as will each success, a signpost in the maps that you write.

You've got this!

For more resources, go to www.resiliencetemplate.com

The Resilience Template™ Toolbox

Additional Books by
Carol Hickson:

Mindfulness For Transformation by Shamash Alidina & Teach Mindfulness Community (Contributing Author)

Coming soon, Autumn 2021: The Resilience Template™ Workbook.

Carol Hickson is available for resilience workshops, CPD training or to speak at your business event.

Call (0044)7899806494, email carol@carolhickson.co.uk or visit www.carolhickson.co.uk for booking information.

You Are Invited!

Carol Hickson offers seminars, and CPD/Inset Day training on Insomnia, the Menopause, Mental Resilience for Adults and Young People, and Stress in the Workplace.

Visit www.carolhickson.co.uk for details.

Learn strategies which will change your life.

Call 0044 (0)7899806494

Email carol@carolhickson.co.uk

Join us on Facebook at *Resilience Template – Mental Health, Be Proactive, Not Reactive.*

Printed in Great Britain
by Amazon